Creation
and
Evolution

CREATION
and
EVOLUTION

by

Jan Lever

Professor of Zoology
at the
Free University at Amsterdam

Translated from the Dutch
by Peter G. Berkhout, M.S., M.D.

GRAND RAPIDS INTERNATIONAL PUBLICATIONS
DISTRIBUTED BY KREGEL'S　　Grand Rapids 6, Michigan
1958

This American Edition
issued by special arrangement with
N. V. GEBR. ZOMER & KEUNING
Wageningen, The Netherlands

Library of Congress Catalog Card Number 57—13247

PRINTED IN THE UNITED STATES OF AMERICA

PREFACE

The problem of how the Christian should approach the origin of organisms in connection with the present status of investigation in the field of natural science has already put in motion many pens.

The opinions which have been launched concerning this from the orthodox side have been, nearly without exception, variations upon fundamentalistic and supranaturalistic themes. This meant that everyone who could not identify himself with these views in every respect soon would get the warning that he was on the wrong road and that he permitted himself to be influenced too much by the quasi-certainties of natural science. In studying the history of the Christian attitude regarding the problem of origin, however, one makes the surprising discovery that both the fundamentalistic and the supranaturalistic approaches themselves originated from a strong orientation to quasi-certainties of natural science (of a few centuries ago). Hence we should consider them least of all capable of being fundamentally Christian. The biologist who has become conscious of this and who nevertheless is convinced of the fact that his Christian belief must be of decisive value for his adjustment to the problems of the origin, meaning and purpose of life, concludes that there must be another way out.

This book, which originated from the tension of this situation, is an attempt to find this new way.

J. L.

CONTENTS

*Creation
and
Evolution*

CHAPTER ONE

THE BIBLE AND REALITY

A few years ago the well-known Swiss zoologist A. Portmann wrote: "Measured in relation to the ultimate purpose in the investigation of reality, the theory of evolution is a bold attempt at understanding the meaning of a tremendous mass of facts. However, in all its details it is still the object of criticism and discussion which, in its final inferences, on every side projects beyond the scientific facts into the area of faith."[1]

In this expression we become aware of the great complexity of the problem of evolution. According to Portmann we have to deal here with an imposing quantity of data, with theories and hypotheses which are still in the realm of discussion and with conclusions which extend beyond the restricted territory of exact scientific thought into the sphere of faith and thus also into our view of the world.

---

[1]A. Portmann, *Biologische Fragmente zu einer Lehre vom Menschen*, Basel, (1951, p. 15).

Many modern scientists are of the opinion that our worldview may come to realization only along the road that runs via scientifically ascertained facts, over hypotheses and theories.

For the Christian the situation is different. For him there are in his worldview definite essential elements which are obtained through faith, entirely independent of and uninfluenced by what is ascertained scientifically. When in addition we think of the fact that one's world-and-life view, without doubt, is not only influenced by science, but also on the other hand independent from the way in which one obtains his worldview, that the statement of problems, theories and hypotheses may be influenced by the worldview of the investigator, then it is important that before we examine the scientific problems we ask as Christians what we *believe* concerning the origin of living organisms and to what extent this faith influences our technical scientific thinking.

As we have stated, the Christian does not build his world-and-life-view exclusively from factors that originate in the sphere of science, but he already has definite certainties. These he derives from the Bible. We can thus reduce the problem to the question of how far the Bible is of importance to us when we think about the origin of things. Does Scripture give us only some general directions for our worldview, or does it give us standards whereby we should judge theories and hypotheses; or is it even possible that the Bible gives us data to which we should adhere in our scientific work?

This question is of great importance when we study the history of the problem of evolution. We can state that the founders of it went through this problem with great difficulty. The positive statements of their later views were greatly influenced by this struggle. When Darwin in 1831-1836 made his journey around the world in the navy brig *The Beagle* he still accepted the Bible as literal truth. At that time the Bible still had for him some value as far as data was concerned. When in 1844 he writes to a friend that he has come to the conclusion that the species are not constant, he states that he feels "like confessing a murder."[2] His view concerning the interpretation of Scripture

---

[2] Letter to Hooker, Jan. 11, 1844: *Life and Letters of Charles Darwin*, II. p.23.

changed very gradually. We find expressions in which he states that it began to occur to him that we should give the Old Testament no more credence than the holy books of the Hindus; that the strongest proofs would be necessary to make a man with common sense believe in the miracles of Christianity; that the more we learn about the fixed laws of nature the more do these miracles become unbelievable, and so on.

At first he hoped that someday letters of eminent Roman writers would be found that would confirm in a most striking way what is written in the Gospels. Although hesitating and doubting, finally the last spark of the Christian belief disappeared: "Thus disbelief crept over me at a very slow rate, but was at last complete. The rate was so slow that I felt no distress."[3]

We thus see in the case of Darwin, who it is interesting to note studied for the ministry, that there was within him a very conscious struggle between the Bible and science.

His friend Thomas H. Huxley went through the same process. He also came from a family in which the Bible was considered to have authority over all of life. Huxley describes how as a child he was educated in Christian doctrine, whereby the cosmogony of Genesis was taught by parents and teachers. When he was twenty-five years of age, in 1850, after a prolonged struggle, he at last freed himself from this. What was left and what he always retained was the view that there probably was at the beginning a pre-existent Being of one kind or another who as the first cause produced this universe. According to him Scripture no longer had any significance for science. Only in the domain of his world-philosophy was there still left a small, unrecognizable deistic fragment.

It was Huxley's view that faith played a very small part in science: "The one act of faith in the convert to science is the confession of the universality of order and of the absolute validity, in all times and under all circumstances, of the law of causation."[4]

---

[3] *Autobiography of Charles Darwin*, The Thinkers Library, No. 7, 6th ed., London, 1949, p. 144.

[4] *Life and Letters of Charles Darwin*, II p. 200.

His worldview is one of rigid, absolute, autonomous laws, purely mechanistic. However, the possibility of the existence of a Being who set the machinery of the world in motion should not be excluded. He points out, therefore, that according to him this idea is not at all in conflict with theism. But: "That with which it does collide, and with which it is absolutely inconsistent, is the conception of creation, which theological speculators have based upon the history narrated in the opening of the book of Genesis."[5]

Also the German founder of evolutionism, Ernst Haeckel, has occupied himself with the problem of the significance of the Bible in regard to science. He also came to the conclusion that this significance is zero. He even believed that faith in the Bible had done much damage to the development of science. He was of the opinion, therefore, that science should be used in the struggle against the Christian belief in creation as derived from Scripture: "The omnipotence of the inflexible laws of nature should be demonstrated against the ancient mystical conceptions of the technical work of a personal Creator."[6] Thus also with Haeckel the laws of nature have taken the place of the Creator and the Ruler of the Universe. Hence we can state definitely that the founders of evolutionism battled against the idea of the Christian faith that Scripture should have influence in the sphere of the exact sciences and that they turned away in large measure from this conception of Christianity that was unacceptable to them.

Since that time many orthodox Protestants have traveled the same difficult road. Also for that reason it is important that we discuss in advance the question concerning the boundaries of the significance of Scripture in connection with the problem of evolution.

The statement of the fact that during the last hundred years many biologists and many investigators of nature from orthodox Protestant circles bade farewell to the church because of this question, and that they lost their Christian faith, should compel

---

[5] *Ibid*, p. 203.
[6] E. Haeckel, *Das Weltbild von Darwin und Lamarck*, Leipzig, 1909, p. 13.

us to ask ourselves whether these boundaries have not been drawn too far or in wrong places. And if that is true would not many receive satisfaction and would it not be refreshing if this were generally recognized?

Also today we often meet with the view in orthodox Protestant groups that Genesis does not only give us truths for our faith, but also concrete data to which the biologist should hold on in his technical work. This opinion includes the view that Genesis, in addition to the proclamation of creation and salvation, gives us indeed exact scientific knowledge, so that the biologist who believes in Scripture should not only confront the Bible and exact science with each other, but that he should measure the truth of scientific data by the literal statements in Scripture. We can designate this opinion as fundamentalistic. This is undoubtedly a strong view and we do well to take definite cognizance of it when we repudiate it.

This rejection we will center at what seems to us the most obvious point. The fundamentalistic view, namely, carries the texts of Genesis deeply into scientific territory and thus brings them into contact with the rise and fall in our thinking concerning detail-questions; and it wants us to make there a choice accordingly. At the same time we wish to emphasize how this opinion resulted from an extreme adaptation of the interpretation of the first chapters of the Bible to the status of science of a few centuries ago.

For what else does this view do than to posit the idea that Genesis is written in technical scientific language and that in the manner as they were defined a few centuries ago? This has led us into debates that are endless and unedifying. We shall discuss a few examples:

a. When Genesis 1 speaks repeatedly of "days," then fundamentalism, or views which are strongly influenced by it, effects a discussion of the problem of the duration of these days. To some it is very clear that here are meant days of 24 hours and they consider it sin to think otherwise. They forget, to stay at the same level of thought, that the sun, with which night and day originated on this earth, was created only on the fourth day; that we do not have to and that it is impossible to connect the divine Sabbath with the rotation of the earth around its axis;[7] and also that a day has a longer duration than 24 hours at the North Pole and at the South Pole. From this last statement it should be clear that the concept *"day"* has a content which is due to mutual agreement (24 hours). This is a convenient physical concept which is useful in practice over the greater part of the earth. If all people lived at the poles, it most likely would not exist in this form. We cannot and may not formulate, already for this very reason, what we should understand by the "days" of Genesis. They simply are not to be formulated on a physical basis of time. Thus to carry them over into the conceptual apparatus of technical knowledge is without sense and is not permissible. This too implies that it is fallacious to equate the "days" with periods, say, of a hundred million years, because this also has its origin in the idea that they have a physical duration of time. Every definition and interpretation of them within a physical measure of time is artificial and human. They constitute an *order* in this sense that Genesis tells us first of all that God has created everything.[8] Also, their succession may not be viewed in the sense that the one followed the other physically. Their meaning does not lie in the area of exact science but in the sphere of a decidedly religious faith. That in this sense they have influence again in the sphere of science is a different matter and will be discussed later.

b. The same is true concerning the word "kind" ("after their kind") which occurs repeatedly in Genesis. Many have understood thereby, and many still do so today, that by this word is meant that God created the recent species, which are known and distinguished by modern biology. We have seen already how Darwin felt as if he committed a murder when he came to the conclusion that the species are variable. However, when we study the history of the biological concept of this word, we draw the conclusion very soon that the term "species" formerly had a much more general connotation. Only 250 years ago was the

---

[7] V. Hepp, *Calvinism and the Philosophy of Nature*, Grand Rapids, 1930, p. 215: "I just want to state my own opinion that the length of those days was not determined by the sun, but by the rotation of the earth upon its axis."

[8] Cf. for a more detailed argumentation about this "cadre"-idea: N. H. Ridderbos, *Is There a Conflict Between Genesis I and Natural Science?*, Grand Rapids, 1957.

present biological interpretation given to it. This signifies that when we equate "kind" with "species" (in the biological sense) we attribute to the writer of Scripture a concept at which biology has arrived only relatively recently through mutual agreement. The unpleasant conflict about evolution has been caused to a large extent by this error in judgment on the part of fundamentalism. Because if "kind" is not equal to "species" then a proven change in species of plants and animals can be accepted readily without impinging upon one's faith.

c. A third instance has reference to the word *"earth."* When this is used in Genesis 1:1 ("In the beginning God created the heavens and the earth") then this word naturally comprises the whole earth as we know it, because this text points to all of created reality. However, when in later verses, where Genesis speaks of "the earth" in the narrower sense (only the earth) and we ascribe to it the meaning of "terrestrial globe," then we attribute to the writer of Scripture an *astronomical* concept that was devised only a few hundred years ago. We then arrive at difficulties that are uncomfortable and that cannot be disentangled. For instance the Flood which covered the whole "earth"; was this the terrestrial globe or was it "the earth" as it was known to the writer of Scripture?

In the first instance, and this is generally defended by fundamentalism,[9] we will have to accept because it follows the same line of thought that all the "species" of animals that we know were present in the Ark of Noah. Of the clean animals and of the birds there were seven pairs, of the unclean one pair. There are known at present about 15,000 species of birds. This means that there were 210,000 birds in the ark. Of the insects we know 800,000 species. If we consider them unclean (this was not the case with all of them, see Leviticus 11) then we come to the conclusion that there were 1,600,000 of them in the ark. The lowest estimate of the number of animals in the ark then would be fully 2,500,000. And then we have not even made mention of the enormous quantity of food that would have to be taken along to feed all those animals for a whole year (see Genesis 6:21).

---

[9] E. Y. Monsma, *If Not Evolution, What Then?*, Grand Rapids, 1954.

It speaks for itself that the ark could not contain all this. This means that fundamentalism itself, if it should reason consistently, must come to the conclusion that the Flood did not spread itself over the entire globe and that the terminology "the earth" may not be equated with the globe as we now know it on the basis of our scientific investigation.[10]

The above-mentioned examples make it plain (and in the succeeding chapters this will be demonstrated more clearly) that fundamentalism to a large extent owes its origin to an interpretation of Scripture with the aid of the natural science of a few centuries ago.

This statement is remarkable because fundamentalism accuses those Christians who think differently of having borrowed ideas from natural science and that they have been sucked into the draft of its materialistic tendencies. The fact is that fundamentalism unconsciously mirrors modern natural science in that of a few centuries ago and then canonizes the latter with texts from Scripture.

We have thus demonstrated that such words as "day," "kind," and "earth" may not be equated with similar concepts defined by natural science. The obvious mistake of fundamentalism is that it takes the account of origins as related in Genesis and reads it as if it were written in the terminology of natural science, and then it turns around and considers the distorted texts as normative for science. When we are once convinced that the concepts of natural science depend on concurrence among men then we see at once clearly that by the method of the fundamentalists we read Scripture wrongly and also that we fetter science unjustly.

A conspicuous example of such a to-and-fro reasoning we find in the well-known book of Aalders, which for the rest has many valuable points. He asks the question whether the animals were created in a mature or an immature stage. His answer is: "Of the birds we read that immediately after creation they 'fly'; in the terminology of God's creating them it says: 'let birds *fly* above the earth in the open firmament of heaven' (Gen. 1:20). We know

---

[10] See concerning the many hypotheses about the Flood, for example, B. Ramm, *The Christian View of Science and Scripture*, Grand Rapids, 1955, pp. 229-249.

that as a rule young birds are not yet able to fly. Hence we can conclude from this that birds at any rate were created mature. But if this is valid in the case of birds then we can also accept it as true for the other animals; because it would be very strange that birds would be an exception in this respect."[11]

One of the consequences of fundamentalism is also that it leads us to the opinion that with the investigation of nature we can prove with exact certitude the contents of our faith. A recent example of this we find in Stoner.[12] This author, who for the rest adjusts classic fundamentalism somewhat to the results of modern investigation, declares that we can point to the correctness of the divine origin of Scripture along mathematical lines. Thus he records that in the first chapter of Genesis there are thirteen events that are described in a definite order. According to him it has been shown in the last fifty years by natural science that not only have all these events taken place exactly as they are described in Scripture, but above all, the order is exactly right. He then asks: "Now what chance did Moses have when writing this first chapter (of Genesis) of getting the thirteen items all accurate and in a satisfactory order? Using the estimates that we have just suggested, we must multiply them all together, and as a result we find that Moses had one chance in 31,135,104,000,000,000,000,000 of getting both the items and the order accurate." This chance is so infinitesimally small that Moses himself never could have written Genesis 1. Stoner's conclusion is therefore: "God wrote such an account in Genesis so that in these latter days, when science has greatly developed, we would be able to verify his account and know for a certainty that God created this planet and the life on it. We cannot doubt that God wrote this book we call the Bible."[13] When we consider the fact that at various points the order of Genesis 1 does not harmonize with that which modern science thinks it has established; moreover, that every investigator of nature confesses that our views constantly change; and finally, that also the successive order in Genesis 2 is largely the opposite of Genesis 1, then not only

---

[11]G. C. Aalders, *De Goddelijke Openbaring in de eerste drie hoofdstukken van Genesis*, Kampen, 1932, p. 273.

[12] P. W. Stoner, *Science Speaks*, Wheaton, Ill., 1952.

[13] A similar method of reasoning is followed by J. De Vries, *Beyond the Atom*, Grand Rapids, 1948.

does this "proof" fall by the wayside, but then also within this fundamentalistic thinking the disastrous possibility exists that the proof for the opposite may be found.

This exposes the dangerous nucleus of fundamentalism. One of its cardinal errors is that it wishes to establish the validity of our faith by exact proofs. Through this, faith and intellect on the one hand, and revelation and science on the other hand, mingle *entirely* into each other's area. The result of this has been a rationalistic faith and a false science and, as honest consequences, doubt and unbelief (Darwin).

These errors of fundamentalism should not close our eyes to the fact that the sources from which this reasoning came were those who were faithful and adhered strictly to the Bible as the Word of God for the totality of our lives and thus also for every branch of science.

Even though we have to describe the further effects of fundamentalism as dangerous and simplistic and have to reject these as such, we should hold tenaciously to this same core of truth. For there is the danger that after what we have said we should go to the other extreme and reach the conclusion that Scripture should not have any influence in the sphere of natural scientific thinking, but that it is written only for the central part of our faith and that it has scientific value only in theology. This opinion, which we also meet today in orthodox-protestant circles, denies that the first chapters of Genesis have reference to *this reality,* which has already been investigated to a very large extent by science. It posits two realities, one for the realm of faith and the other for that of experience, both of which are true, but without points of contact. If we definitely wish to hold on to what is denied here, then we will have to ask ourselves the question, in which sense does Genesis have significance for science? In answering this question we will have to proceed as Christians from the principle that Scripture is a miracle. And this because the Bible gives us data about reality which no science can *discover;* for example, that there exists a personal God who called all things into being. Scripture is thus in a certain sense a lamp, we believe, which places reality in the proper light, also our reality which we have to investigate. But the Bible is not a magic lantern which communicates to us exact scientific data in the form of tables, graphs and concepts.

Thus Genesis, in a miraculous way, *reveals* to us the main motives for the existence and the origin of this world and this human life. It does this, however, in a concrete manner. Scripture does not say: God has made everything, there was no sin originally, this came into existence only after the Fall, and so on. It is not a theoretical treatise. No, the Bible says that God made birds, fish, man. God speaks about man by name and surname, about a garden of Eden, about trees and fruits. Scripture tells us that the revealed realities which are not to be discovered through natural science are irrevocably linked with those that can be investigated through natural science. Thus the concrete language of Scripture is for us essential in its very concreteness. We are told that *this* world, this human being, that what has been created good, this sin, this redemption are indissolubly connected, and cut into the sphere of this reality and this history.

Hence Genesis deals with that reality which we can investigate scientifically and mentions data which we cannot discover scientifically. But Geneses does this in such a way, and that is essential for our reasoning, that we may not consider the language that is used as scientific concepts, indeed, not at all as scientifically qualified language. This signifies that the Bible usually tells us *that* something has happened, but not *how* it happened. The *how* sometimes lies in the terrain of science. The Bible gives us the high points, science *sometimes* can discover the lines between them. We can never derive from Scripture exact physical, astronomical and biological knowledge, and thus also not exact historical knowledge. The Bible simply is not for that purpose.

To express it still more clearly, it is our opinion that Genesis has been written to reveal realities for us that are of eternal, fundamental religious significance and which cannot be discovered through science. These revealed realities we should accept gratefully and we should lay them as normative at the basis also of our scientific thinking. These revealed realities have no *concrete* contact with our investigation. They cannot be investigated and they cannot be imprisoned in our scientific-human concepts. These revealed realities have unfolded themselves in our concrete reality in order that they should be placed in relation to us, as is made clear to us by the choice of communication of Scripture. This concrete reality through which these scientifically uncapturable realities operate and have operated (we could also call it the substratum of these scientifically unattainable realities) is of the same nature as that which is studied through natural science. This offers the possibility of fields of contact. But in this area Genesis is no longer normative for observational science, simply because it is not the purpose of Genesis to supply us with data in the form in which we can find them ourselves (in principle) by means of investigation, and also because Genesis is not a scientific manuscript. If that were so then the realities that cannot be found and described through scientific investigation, as a matter of logic, could not have gotten into the Bible. Hence, we should be grateful that Scripture is a non-scientific book!

That Scripture is not normative in the territory of substrata does not signify that its communications concerning this do not have to be true, but it only means that the method and the conceptual apparatus which the Bible uses is not scientific. To put the significance and the normativity of the first chapters of Genesis thus makes it possible for us to view the problem of evolution without the tendency to incline the letter of Genesis and the scientific data artificially towards each other, and without the necessity that an apparent discrepancy has significance for our faith.

The question concerning the points of contact of the substrata with the scientific data will be discussed in the succeeding chapters. It is proper, however, at this time to point out yet a few revealed realities in Genesis that are not to be discovered through scientific investigation and to consider to what extent in a general sense (the details follow later) they exert influence within the domain of science.

The first truth which Genesis reveals to us is, of course, that of the *origin* of the world. This is expressed in the well-known words to which every Christian subscribes: "I believe in God the Father, the Almighty, Creator of heaven and earth." This signifies to the Christian that the wealth of structural form of this world did not originate as a game of chance, but that there exists a personal God, who as a Father has brought it all into being. That this faith is also of importance for science is clear, because science also has to occupy itself with the question concerning the origin of life and of the world. And science, separated from faith in the Creator, selects other points of departure; for example, the eternity of laws and of things. Against this the Christian will posit that the entire structural wealth of this reality is created. Let it be said immediately that it is not possible for us to point out *how* creation took place and *what, in concreto,* is produced through creation; because, as a matter of fact, this lies not only outside of our perceptive but also of our conceptual faculty. The knowledge that a divine creation has taken place does not make it necessary for us, for the sake of the completeness of our world-view, to accept or to propagate a definite hypothesis concerning the origin of a subdivision. On the contrary, faith in creation makes us hesitate to accept easy solutions and gives us scientific freedom to state that proofs for a certain opinion are adequate or not and, for the time being, to leave a cardinal question entirely open scientifically. There will be ample opportunity in the future to point to this liberty which Christians, according to many out-siders and insiders, lack in the sphere of science.

The second reality which Scripture reveals to us is that of *meaning.* When we wish to confine our thinking only to that which can be observed, then we reach the conclusion that this world is stiflingly meaningless, or that it has its meaning within itself. The Bible throws a light upon this world by means of which we begin to see that its meaning lies outside of itself, that it exists according to God's will and for God, to his glory. This also has practical, particular significance for the investigator him-self who now sees the majesty of God in all that he investigates and who constantly and rightly comes under the impression of this idea of meaning.

A third reality which is closely related to the preceding is that of the immanent *purpose* of the creation. If we remain only on the level of the scientific data, then we come to the conclusion that man is an accidental and probably a passing product of nature. In Genesis it is revealed to us that the entire creation was directed to man, so that all other things and organisms are entitled to an entourage-function for this being created after the image of God and that man is equipped with all kinds of capacities that the other creatures do not possess; a being who has the germ of eternity and who can glorify God consciously and who can get into contact with him.

That this knowledge which Scripture grants us is of importance within the technical field speaks for itself; because there we are reminded of the fact that the origin of man is principially of a different kind than that, for example, of a horse. In addition we thereby notice a planned directional line operating through the history of the origin of the world.

When we finally wish to give an answer to the question, which we stated at the beginning, where lie the boundaries of the influence the Bible would exercise upon our thinking, then we have to presuppose that Scripture demands first of all our entire faith and thereupon, in an important measure, all spheres of life. Via this the Bible makes its influence felt in the area of theories and hypotheses in the sense that it gives direction— erroneous theories are curtailed, and a critical attitude is stimulated. The Bible, however, offers no technicological theories or hypotheses and especially not exact technical scientific data. Scripture does not give us data which we can find for ourselves, but it is a revelation of realities that lie outside of our ability to discover. We can also state it this way: Scripture reveals a series of powerful realities which form in the believer the pattern for his world-and-life view and are there of such overpowering significance that they, as such or further effectuated or applied, penetrate irresistibly within his technicological thinking. Thus in principle, in extreme cases, they may determine the arrangement of his data. Scientific data are not given. Man can find these himself because they exist by the grace of God and because man has been created after the image of God in such a way that he can find them.

Now only, after this repudiation of fundamentalism, can we really approach the problem of the relationship between creation and evolution. Because only thus can we review seriously the biological data that have been discovered during the last century and which are interpreted in the light of the concept- and the hypothesis-complex of evolutionary thought. We are not now, for example, forced to reject in advance the view that the earth has existed millions of years or that the species of organisms can vary.

And when we state the problem of creation and evolution, we notice with our limited intellect that there are really three chief possibilities as far as their "relation" is concerned. Because they play a role in the following chapters they are enumerated now at this point. Not till the last chapter will they be reviewed extensively.

1. *First,* that all types of plants and animals in the progress of time have been created and that they possess only to a small degree the possibility of evolutionary development.

2. The *second* one is this, that only at cardinal points in the realization of this world in time were essentially new structures created: matter at the beginning, life after some time, the animal psyche later and the human spiritual structures only a relatively short time ago. The further unfolding took place through a developmental process.

3. The *third* possibility is this, that "in the beginning" all aspects of reality were created which in the course of time thus successively were realized through a developmental process of that which was created.

According to the first view creation has occurred frequently during the course of time, according to the second only a few times and, according to the last, never, except that it must have taken place at the very beginning of time and only through it did time originate. The first two views have this thought in common, that the creation *in time* penetrated into this reality. This signifies that if our investigation advances far enough, we will be able to point out and to discover when and where this creation took place. Since creation, however, as an act of God in every form escapes human grasp and comprehension, the logical possibility of establishing dates and places should be an indication that these first two possibilities lead to great difficulties. Yet, these are the possibilities which momentarily have the greatest numbers of adherents among Christians.

We should perceive, however, that only the radical opinion that this reality is one whole, which in all its aspects in the beginning had its origin in divine creation, whereby meaning and purpose were given, is able to conquer these difficulties. Only with this thought can we do justice to the Christian faith *and* to the data which nature gives us.

In the following chapters we shall review the scientific data concerning various central problems about the origin of flora and fauna (the origin of life, of types of organisms, of species and of man), together with various methods of interpreting them. At the end of each chapter we shall trace the usual approach to the problem on the part of orthodox Protestants. This method of approach will be reviewed critically.

In the final chapter the central discussion will be the significance of the theme "Creation and Evolution" for our biological thinking. An attempt will be made to point to the way out of the contradictions of current opinions.

Finally, in this volume mention will be made often of creationism as a counterpart to evolutionism. By creationism we understand here every biological approach to the problem of origin which, issuing from the central credo of the Christian church, wishes to confess also in science the creation of this reality and the daily direction of all processes through God.

It will be clear that within this creationism there occur differences of opinion about all kinds of problems.[14] This does not alter the fact that it is necessary for *everyone* who believes in creation to posit this in modern science as a matter for consideration, since without the acknowledgement of this it can never be possible to arrive at a correct picture of this reality.

---

[14]See for an excellent review, B. Ramm, *op. cit.*, 1955.

CHAPTER TWO

THE ORIGIN OF LIFE

1. *Introduction*

The quotation from Portmann with which we began our first chapter included the observation that with the problem of evolution we have to deal with a complex of data, hypotheses and theories in interplay with worldviews. We accepted this description of the problem as correct. The problem of the origin of life gives us ample opportunity to demonstrate that the concept of Portmann indeed portrays the true state of affairs.

In order to understand the meaning of present-day opinions concerning this and in order to see to what great extent they are determined by one's worldview, it is necessary to consider how ideas concerning the origin of life have developed in the course of time and how they have changed.

2. *Greek Antiquity and the Middle Ages*

Already with the pre-Socratic natural philosophers the approach to this problem was governed entirely by abstract thinking.

Aside from a few, for example, Anaxagoras, who thought of eternal germs of life, most ancient thinkers accepted the view, on speculative and also religious grounds, that first forms of life originated from water as primitive matter. They adduced factual arguments to support their opinion. For example, they pointed to the fact that all living creatures are saturated with water, that they all develop from fluid material and that they all live on liquid food (Thales). However, their insight as natural scientists was influenced by their worldview. This formed, as it were, a pair of spectacles through which they could see only those arguments which agreed with their views.

The situation was somewhat different in the case of the later Greeks. Aristotle, for example. laid strong emphasis upon observation. The inductive method had to be followed with the problem of the origin of life. He thus came to the idea of *spontaneous generation,* which includes that living organisms can originate spontaneously out of lifeless, often decaying, matter.

To give an example of his way of reasoning let us see how he thought of the origin of eels.[1] He was sure that these fish came into existence neither through copulation nor by means of eggs. With a torrent of arguments he proves that: they have never found roe or spawn in an eel; they have never seen a brood of young ones; when they cut them open they never find exits for sperm or eggs; in some pools that had dried up entirely they found eels all at once after a shower. How do they originate? Aristotle says: "Some writers, however, are of the opinion that they generate their kind, because in some eels little worms are found, from which they suppose that eels are derived. But this opinion is not founded on fact. Eels are derived from the so-called "earth's guts" that grow spontaneously in mud and in humid ground; in fact, eels have at times been seen to emerge out of such earthworms, and on other occasions have been rendered visible when the earthworms were laid open by either scraping or cutting. Such earthworms are found both in the sea and in rivers, especially where there is decayed matter; in the sea in places where seaweed abounds, and in the rivers and marshes near to the edge;

---

[1]Aristoteles, *Historia Animalium,* Book VI, 16. English translation, Oxford, 1910.

for it is near to the water's edge that sunheat has its chief power and produces putrefaction. So much for the generation of the eel."

Aristotle's approach to the problem of origin sounds more modern than that of Thales or that of Anaxagoras, since he puts strong emphasis upon observation. For him spontaneous generation was a natural datum that could be verified every day. But also in his case his philosophy plays a part. The evidence for this is that for him the mechanism of spontaneous generation was no problem. Through his form-matter motif, according to which matter produces only an insignificant coarse material for the essential form, the decaying substances did not have such importance that true investigation made sense.

The first type of opinions we met were entirely philosophical in character, the second an application of a worldview which, because it strongly emphasized observation, made the impression of being convincing and exact. Of great importance was the way in which the first Christian scholars viewed natural science. One could imagine that they rejected radically every form of spontaneous generation, that they indicated God in the beginning had created all organisms and therefore no new life could momentarily come into existence. The very first Christian thinkers thus came into contact with the conflict between (Greek) natural science and the Christian faith. An interesting incidental problem for them was that even at that time natural science estimated the earth to be older than one could figure on the basis of the genealogies of the Bible. The question concerning "days" and "periods" was already urgent for them. It is very instructive for us to consider how they escaped this difficulty. Some Christian scholars thought that they could substitute for the six days of Genesis 1 periods of one thousand years each, since with God a thousand years are as one day (Ps. 90:4; II Peter 3:8). We see that even at that time they used Bible texts as mathematical data in arithmetical calculations. In a similar fashion the principle of spontaneous generation was accepted by Christian thinkers. They were impressed by the seeming abundance of facts supporting the idea of spontaneous generation. It was a "scientific fact" at that time. Therefore they adapted to each other reciprocally their religious conviction about generation and their scientific idea concerning spontaneous generation in such a way that it resulted in a conclusive logic.

The great church father Augustine (354-430) in his line of thought concerning the origin of reality proceeded from the idea that it originated entirely from divine creation. According to him all things were created at the beginning, in harmony with the divine ideas. These ideas were transformed with creation into germs and causes. Through joint action of these, all that was created could develop in the course of time. This does not mean that all the things that we know in reality were present at once after creation in a complete fashion. They were present, but, for the most part, only potentially, in concrete germinal form. Through the direction of divine providence, in the course of time, they could unfold from the already present germs of life and causes. He considers that coming into being a natural process, without the supernatural interference of God.[2] In this light we should consider also the view of Augustine about the phenomenon of spontaneous generation.[3] He begins by pointing out that there are in this world concrete germs of life of all organisms Some of these are visible before our eyes in the form of fruits and eggs, but others are hidden. Especially these hidden germs of life bring about spontaneous generation. They do not originate anew repeatedly (herein lies the core of the adjustment), but they were created. To make clear the meaning of this he gives a very literal interpretation of a few texts in Genesis 1. In verse 11 we read, for example, "And God said, Let the earth put forth grass, herb yielding seed, *and* fruit trees bearing fruit after their kind, wherein is the seed thereof, upon the earth: and it was so." And in verse 20 we read: "And God said, Let the waters swarm with swarms of living creatures, and let the birds fly above the earth in the open firmament of heaven." The germs of life through which spontaneous generation originates, Augustine says, are "those germs from which, at the command of the Creator, the water produced the first swimming and flying creatures and from which the earth produced the first germs of life of its kind

---

[2] Cf. J. H. Diemer, *Natuur en Wonder I*, Philosophia Reformata, 8, 100-128, 1943, pp. 120-125.

[3] Augustine, *De Trinitate* III, 13. Dr. A. Sizoo, Amsterdam called my attention to this passage, for which I extend him my sincere thanks.

and the first living creatures of its kind. Because at that time these germs did not make their appearance for the formation of these beings in such a way that it required all their strength to produce them; but often the proper occasion is lacking for mixing, through which they could make their appearance and finally could complete their kind." Spontaneous generation, according to Augustine, should be attributed to the fact that a great quantity of these hidden germs of life has been left over, through which creation continues unceasingly.

Of Augustine's further application we give one poetic example: "Undoubtedly, the bees receive the seed for their progeny without copulation; but, they gather the seed, which as it were is spread upon the land, with their mouth." We thus see that the phenomenon of spontaneous generation was, for Augustine, not at all in conflict with his Christian faith. To the contrary, it gave confirmation for his Christian-philosophic opinion concerning the origin and the existence of this world.

This remarkable, speculative and for us instructive adaptation of Christian thought to Greek ideas, they tried to confirm with still other texts than those of Genesis 1 already mentioned. For example, they used Exodus 8, verses 16 and 17, where we are told that, when Aaron struck the dust of the earth with his rod, the dust became gnats.

They also viewed it this way, that just as the pregnant mother animal produces new life, but which was present in the germ, so the earth too is pregnant with new living organisms.[4] The "let the earth bring forth" is, in this line of thought, a command which gives "the womb of the earth" its mandate to this day.

During the entire Middle Ages the idea of spontaneous generation was generally accepted by all Christian thinkers. This mixture of faith and science into a quasi-scientific view of apparently factual data satisfied the spirits for a very long time. We still find it in Paracelsus (1493-1541) and also in Harvey (1578-1657). The latter propagated indeed the view *"omne vivum ex ovo"* all living beings proceed from eggs, but with him the concept *"ovo"* had such a broad meaning that it subsumed spontaneous

---

[4] W. Zimmermann, *Evolution*, Freiburg/Munchen, 1953, p. 70.

generation. This does not surprise us after we have taken notice of Augustine's opinion.

That the idea of spontaneous generation, and the opinions connected therewith, were viewed by the biologists of the period 1500-1650 as having reference to perfectly natural processes, is very clear from the fact that in this period there was even experimentation about it. A branch of biology developed which we could name, after the analogy of modern developmental physiology, the spontaneous-generation physiology. We shall describe two such experiments. In the first place, Paracelsus proposes how we can make a human individual, the famous "homunculus," outside the female body *in vitro*. One gathers the human sperm in a cucumber and lays this in the intestinal contents of a horse. This should last about 40 days. Then lively motion starts and a human-like being has already originated. When, after this cucumber-period, we continue to keep the mass for another 40 weeks at the right temperature and feed it every day with human blood, it gradually becomes a living child with all the appertaining limbs. It is only smaller than normal. After this period one does not have to treat it in principle differently from other children; only, it requires extreme care in feeding and the like; but that speaks for itself!

The other example concerns the investigation of the Brussels biologist Van Helmont (1577-1644), the deserving inventor of the method to fabricate mice. Upon the basis of extensive deductions he came to the conclusion that "human sweat" has a strong mice-generating property. To derive full benefit from this one should take a (medieval) dirty shirt and put it in a barrel of grains of wheat. When you let this combination stand for 21 days, the "vapors" of the shirt and of the wheat fuse. Through this process mice are set free. To the amazement of Van Helmont they looked exactly like the mice which see the light of day in the more customary manner. It is clear that one should not put a cover over the barrel because then the young mice will suffocate on account of lack of air!

3. *Experiments Concerning Spontaneous Generation*

This adventurous, flourishing period of bold speculation and surprising experiments was followed by the most attractive and sober period of investigation concerning spontaneous generation. In the 16th, but especially in the 17th century doubt about the scholastic traditions became one of the stimulants to a profound investigation in various fields. Not only alchemy and the conceptions concerning monsters, but also spontaneous generation were tested critically.

The Italian investigator Redi (1626-1694) was the first to fight this idea openly and with convincing arguments. For centuries it had been accepted that flies originate from decaying meat. Redi observed that the "worms" (maggots) which occur in it are the larvae of flies, which, moreover, come forth from eggs laid by flies. As proof he adduced, among other things, that when we keep the flies at a distance by means of a fine net the "worms" do not appear. Very soon the same was found to be correct with the "worms" one meets in apples and pears. Before that it was thought that they came into existence through the dirt that one finds around the "worm" in the fruit. Now they observed that this material, exactly to the contrary, was to be attributed to the presence of the "worm." Through further investigation it became evident that also true worms, beetles, lice, fish, frogs, snakes, mice, lizards and hedgehogs, concerning which it was thought formerly that they came from decaying matter, were produced from eggs or from similar living creatures (e.g. as is the case with most mammals).

Thus it seemed that in the area of biology, where it always had been very dark, clear daylight had finally penetrated. But soon the picture looked darker again. Only shortly after it had been established that all organisms that can be seen with the unaided eye are generated biologically, when a new invention, the microscope, was constructed and the Infusoria, a group of Protozoa, were discovered.

With this discovery the idea of spontaneous generation again became current. When it was observed, for instance, that these Infusoria occur in great numbers in abundant, variegated forms when a dead body was laid in the water, then the idea of spontaneous generation returned again, even though usually in an altered form. Many thought to explain this by adducing that living material after death still has the possibility of life left in it.

Under favorable circumstances it then could unfold itself through spontaneous generation.

Yet there were at the same time other investigators who entertained the view that Infusoria also produced eggs, so that there existed among them a continuous generative relation. It was soon recognized that only experimentation could render a decision. The English cleric Needham (1713-1781) wrote a book in 1745 in which he defended with experiments the spontaneous generation of these organisms. He put fruit juice in a flask and heated it to such a degree that he suspected that all the Infusoria that were present must be dead. Then he sealed the flask hermetically. After some time he could demonstrate the presence of Infusoria in the fluid. This experiment had the result that many eminent biologists, among others de Buffon (1707-1788), accepted again the idea of spontaneous generation.

Over against the views of Needham and de Buffon was that of Bonnet (1720-1793) and successors. These thought that one should accept the pre-existence of germs of life, from which the living organisms could develop when the circumstances were favorable. This was an idea which thus was reminiscent of that of Anaxagoras and of Augustine.

The most outstanding opponent was Spallanzani (1729-1799). In 1765 he wrote a dissertation about the question of spontaneous generation and the views of Needham and de Buffon. Spallanzani repeated among others, the experiments of Needham. He maintained that only when all the materials and also the air in the flask have been heated to a high degree and all contacts with the surrounding air made impossible—and if one after that still finds Infusoria then only has proof for spontaneous generation been delivered. He took 19 flasks, closed them hermetically after he had put vegetable matter in them, and let them boil for an hour. After this no Infusoria made their appearance.

Needham was not at all convinced through this experiment. According to him Spallanzani had handled the material too carelessly. Through the continuous boiling the "vegetative power" had disappeared and, in addition, the little amount of air had been spoiled. Therefore Needham proposed to Spallanzani to repeat the experiments and to continue the boiling only long enough till the eventual germ of life had been killed. Then he might close his vessels hermetically after he had admitted a small amount of fresh air. In order to destroy the germs of life which might possibly be present in the air, he might lay the vessels a few minutes in boiling water, "as long as a chicken egg needs to get hard." If Spallanzani then, after the lapse of some time, could no longer find any Infusoria, Needham would consider himself vanquished.

Spallanzani executed the experiment carefully according to the recipe of Needham and found Infusoria. But when he boiled the material 45 minutes then all life became permanently impossible. The well-known French investigator Gay-Lussac (1778-1850) analysed the air in vessels of that kind and found that no oxygen could be demonstrated in them. This reduced the value of the negative experiments, since of course, even if eventually Infusoria could originate, this would be made impossible because of the lack of oxygen.

For that reason Schwann (1810-1882) in 1837 investigated the possibility of admitting fresh air into the vessels. He flushed the vessels with air that had been heated shortly but intensely in a basin of boiling mercury. In these vessels no Infusoria appeared. Through Pasteur (1822-1895) in 1862 an end was made to the struggle concerning spontaneous generation of Infusoria, since he showed that the apparently spontaneous appearance of these organisms is always the result of definite, very small stages of life, such as encapsulated spores, which as particles of dust are present just about everywhere in the atmosphere. He proved this through extensive experiments by gathering in glass flasks, with sterilized nutrient broth air from very different sources: from cellars, from meadows, but also from mountains 6,700 feet high. His experiments finally convinced the whole scientific world that the origin of Infusoria could be traced back in every instance to germs of life. And with that fell at the same time the last vestige of the apparent proof for and observation of spontaneous generation. It was now demonstrated fully that not alone rats and mice, spiders and snails, insects and worms cannot originate in this fashion, but that even the smallest known organisms can produce only new generations via *living* stages.

When we ask ourselves concerning the period of about 1600-1850, in   which the idea of spontaneous generation gradually disappeared after difficult experimentation, whether the worldview of the investigator had any influence upon his view concerning this question, then we can answer that the spiritual climate caused by the Christian background was favorable for the investigation. We saw that the idea of spontaneous generation could easily be Christianized. But also a world without this phenomenon would not bring into difficulty the Christian faith. People were free and for the most part without philosophical prejudice regarding this problem.

4. *Classical Evolutionism and the Origin of Life*

This situation has become entirely different during the last century. And it should be emphasized that this change has had two causes. In the first place, a great number of fossils were found of beings that looked entirely different from recent ones. Initially they were viewed as sports (freaks) of nature, *"lusus naturae,"* or as "previews" which God executed in stone before he created the organisms. Very soon these solutions did not satisfy any longer. There arose in many a mind ideas that took a different direction than had been customary up to this time. The first cause for a changed view about the question concerning the origin of life thus came from observation.

The second cause was from the philosophical and the religious side. We saw in the previous chapter how many of the most eminent investigators of the last century bade farewell to the Christian faith. They thus also lost an all-embracing world-and-life-view and it is not surprising that they looked for a new one. This they found in materialism, which adjusted itself in an easier way to the new findings than did the Christian worldview and the interpretation of Scripture at that time.

We see therefore that the change of direction in natural science was caused by the finding of new data, but also through the conception of a new worldview. This is a worldview according to which the only thing that exists is nature, which is dominated by autonomous, even-constant uniformitarian laws of nature (principle of causality) ; while by means of further elaboration it denied that there exist any essential differences between "spirit," "soul," "life" and "matter." Materialistic monism reduced all aspects of reality to the physical-chemical.

No one will deny that this view had its birth in cogitation and not through the exact method from data derived from natural science. It is interesting to explore how this worldview which, in saturated or diluted form still captivates the minds of the majority of investigators, took hold of the problem of the origin of life. Proceeding from these premises the only conceivable possiblity is an evolution from crystal to living beings, *"vom Kristall zum Lebewesen"* and "from amoeba to man."

We find this already in the first evolutionistic work, *Philosophie Zoologique* which was written in 1809 by the Frenchman Lamarck (1744-1829). In this book we find all the aspects of the core of the theory of evolution extensively expounded. This implies, according to him, among others: "That all the organic creatures of our globe are true productions of nature which she wrought successively through long periods of time." This means: "That in its progress nature began and begins again to fashion most simple organic bodies every day, and that she forms these alone directly; that is to say, only the rudiments of their organization indicated by the term *générations spontanées.*"[5]

When we consider that Lamarck wrote this book before Pasteur definitely disproved that Infusoria arise by spontaneous generation, then we can understand why he wrote thus about these organisms. He says about them: "It is only in the case of animals of this kind that nature seems to form spontaneous or direct generations and that she regenerates them unceasingly whenever the circumstances are favorable; and we are attempting to show that through them she has the possibility to produce indirectly, during an enormous period of time, all the other races of animals which we know.

"That which warrants us to think that the Infusoria, or most of these animals, owe their existence to spontaneous generations is that these fragile animals all perish with the lowering of the temperature during unfavorable seasons; and one surely cannot suppose that bodies so delicate are able to leave any germ of

---

[5] J. B. Lamarck, *Philosophie Zoologique*, Ed. 1907, pp. 45-46.

life of such stability that they can be preserved and reproduce themselves in warmer times."[6]

From these Infusoria, according to Lamarck, all living beings originated. They had the capacity for growth, respiration, reproduction and the like, and they were able to adapt themselves to all kinds of circumstances. Definite forms broke through the winter barrier. They were able to retain the acquired characters and thus to make them hereditary. In this fashion finally the higher forms arose.

If in the case of Lamarck the idea of spontaneous generation was irrevocably connected with his evolutionary views, Charles Darwin (1809-1882) was somewhat more careful. In his *The Origin of Species by Means of Natural Selection* (1859) he refers in connection with this question to Lamarck and he adds that science has not proved this hypothesis to be true, but that it might possibly do so in future.

Under the influence of Haeckel (1834-1919) whom we shall discuss presently, the consequence is forced upon Darwin. Thus he writes in 1871, in *The Descent of Man,* that there are organisms among the Protozoa that consist only of formless bits of primitive slime or protoplasm. From these primitive organisms the higher must have developed. These primitive organisms, called Monera, owe their existence originally to spontaneous generation.

This Monera-hypothesis of Haeckel opens a new era in the opinions regarding the origin of life. Through the researches of Pasteur it was proved that not even the smallest known organisms originated through spontaneous generation. This meant that the entire present-day flora and fauna propagate themselves only through a continuous genetic process. One would think that after a long difficult struggle of twenty centuries to escape from the apparent observation of spontaneous generation, everyone finally would have rejoiced to hold on to these facts. The remarkable phenomenon, however, presents itself that the idea of spontaneous generation, which had landed in science because it was stated simply as a datum, was declared as something that was self-

---

6 J. B. Lamarck, ibid., pp. 178-179.

evident in the field of science at the same moment that the data which pleaded for it fell apart.

The importance of the scientific nature of this idea we find emphasized in Haeckel who says clearly: "Among the various hypothetical presentations about the origin of life upon the earth, which struggled among themselves in a lively fashion only a short time ago, there is finally only one hypothesis that is valid, and which is in harmony with the newer physics and physiology: — the hypothesis of *Archigonie* (or 'abiogenesis' in a definite, entirely limited sense!) This hypothesis, which we consider the only natural one, consists of the following suppositions: 1. The organisms with which the spontaneous origin of life began, were *Monera* or *Probionts,* 'organisms without organs,' very small homogeneous plasma-bodies without anatomical structure. 2. The viability of these first Monera, which were composed of like plasma-molecules, limited itself to assimilation and growth; if at last the definite cohesive boundary was overstepped the tiny particle parted into two pieces (the beginning of propagation and, at the same time, of inheritance). 3. The homogeneous plasma of these Monera-bodies arises as albumen by a chemico-synthetic process from inorganic combinations:—from water, carbon dioxide and ammonia (most likely by interaction of definite acids:—nitric acid, cyanic acid and others)."[7]

When we keep in mind that in the days of Haeckel every datum supporting this archigony was lacking and that at the same time the idea of spontaneous generation always had been upheld by the data then the following addition of Haeckel sounds almost humorous: "The acceptance of *archigony* in this strongly defined concept is the only hypothesis which explains in a *scientific* way the origin of organic life on our planet; it should not be confused with those manifold hypotheses, which are partly or entirely unscientific, which, since days of old, were thrown together under the vague concept of 'Urzeugung' *generatio aequivoca* or *spontanea.*"

Sometimes it was thought that the Monera had been found. Thus, for example, in 1868, with the laying of the first telegraph cable from England to America, mud samples were taken from the bottom of the Atlantic ocean. As usual the material was

---

[7] E. Haeckel. *Systematische Phylogenie*, Vol. I, Berlin, 1894, p. 35 ff.

preserved in alcohol to prevent spoilage. It very soon came into the hands of the English zoologist T. H. Huxley. By microscopic study there seemed to be present fine granules embedded in a gelatinous mass.

It appeared to Huxley that we were dealing here with Monera, the primeval slime about which Haeckel had written. In honor of Haeckel he called it *Bathybius Haeckelii.* Two years later Preyer sent a bottle of deep sea mud from the vicinity of the Faroe Islands to Haeckel. He was immediately very enthusiastic and wrote an illustrated article about it in the *Jenaische Zeitschrift* of 1870. Spontaneous generation was "confirmed," as it had been many a time before. Haeckel wrote: "The fact that unheard-of masses of naked, living protoplasm cover the depths of the oceans in a very preponderant quantity and under very peculiar circumstances, stimulates us to so numerous reflections that one could write a book about it." Very soon, however, it was affirmed that a grandiose mistake had been made. The *Bathybius Haeckelii* proved to be an artifact that results when sea water and alcohol are mixed, a gypsum-like sediment. In 1876 the German naturalist Möbius made it in this way with much hilarity at the Assembly of Naturalists at Hamburg.[8]

When we review what precedes it appears to us that the factual grounds for spontaneous generation gradually melted away in history. At first it was thought that all kinds of animals that can be seen with the unaided eye, such as mice and fish, could originate spontaneously. Later Infusoria were taken into consideration for that purpose. When that proved untenable for organisms of that kind, the Monera-idea arose. This, however, was to have only a short life. With its passing the scientific basis for the theory of spontaneous generation fell away.

Yet history repeated itself again. With the discovery of the viruses the idea of spontaneous generation came to the fore once more in the twentieth century, even though in modified form. These well-known exciters of disease show various characteristics whereby they exhibit themselves as lifeless, others as living bodies. To delineate our thought we shall discuss a few of these characteristics at this point.

---

[8] See concerning this question, L. Huxley, *Thomas Henry Huxley*, London, 1920, p. 69ff.; J. Schmutzer, *Prof. Ernst Haeckel*, Leiden, 1907, p. 82.

Some arguments which plead against viruses being alive is the fact that they are too small to contain the necessary enzymes (compounds that cause reactions, such as digestion, to proceed rapidly), which are characteristic of living protoplasm. In addition, they exhibit no respiration and cannot propagate themselves outside living cells. But, above all, the established ability for different viruses to crystallize is an important argument in favor of their being lifeless.

On the other hand, they exhibit characteristics whereby they resemble living organisms. They possess, type for type, a definite structure (they have thus a specifically constructed "body"). They reproduce themselves (they can multiply themselves, at any rate, inside plants and animals). Some give off waste-products. They can mutate (hereditary change of characters). They possess the ability of adaptation. It is probable that some go through a cycle of development (bacteriophage).[9] Above all, it is an important fact that all viruses contain so-called nucleo-proteins, definite chemical compounds which also occur in all cells of all living organisms and especially in their reproductive parts, such as the chromosomes.

Of the viruses no one can say, therefore, whether they are or are not living beings. Looking at the preceding discussion it is not strange that there are investigators who regard them as typical intermediate steps between the absolutely lifeless and the living. That is why the question of how the viruses originated is important. Concerning this one meets with a number of opinions in our day.[10]

First of all, some writers are of the opinion that viruses—when we consider their chemical similarity with parts of living cells, their ability to reproduce and their mutability—arose from particles which were separated from their places in the structure of the cell and went on to live an independent existence. Various arguments plead for this hypothesis.

---

[9] G. Penso, "Cycle of Phage Development within the Bacterial Cell," *Protoplasma*, 45, pp. 251-263, 1955.

[10] See, for example, W. A. Collier, "Hypothesen over de oorsprong van virus en virus-soorten," *Chronica Naturae*, No. 105, p. 11, 1949; H. L. Booy, *Aan de grens van het leven*, Leiden, 1947; T. H. Thung, *Grondbeginselen der Planten-virologie*, Wageningen, 1949, pp. 7-12; F. C. Bawden, *Plantviruses and Virus Diseases*, Waltham, Mass., 1950, pp. 315-327.

A second opinion follows the generally observed phenomenon that parasitic organisms often exhibit a pronounced reduction of organs in comparison with free-living related forms. Some parasitic animals no longer possess a mouth, intestines, respiratory and circulatory system. They are virtually nothing but little bags of sex-cells. The adherents of this opinion view the viruses as similarly extremely reduced parasitic Infusoria.

Thirdly, some hold the view that the viruses are nothing more than cell-products which are formed anew constantly by the host-cells in which they are found.

These three are the most common ways of explaining the origin of viruses. As indicated, they are all the outcome of the view that the viruses belong to the realm of living organisms; or, to express it more strongly, they owe their existence to living creatures that were present before them. Hence, they cannot have been the ancestors of the plants and animals.

5. *Modern Views*

What precedes makes it possible for us, against the background of history, to consider the present-day views about the origin of life. Before we pass on to this, however, it is of importance to point out the change in construction of the problem in the course of time. The adherents of spontaneous generation were first of the opinion that even today individual living beings could originate. That concerned initially such animals as frogs: later, Infusoria. When this fell by the wayside, it was definite that not a single organism today can originate from lifeless material and contact with the factually observable origin of living beings was lost. With the Monera and the viruses this contact was apparently restored for a time, but it disappeared again with further study. The primeval origin of organisms withdrew itself from observation and research. This had two results. In the first place, from now on there was no longer any talk of the origin of distinct organisms (frogs, Infusoria, Monera), but about the origin of "life," a concept even more difficult to describe than the Monera. In the second place, the absence of data had the result that one's worldview could exercise influence upon scientific hypotheses with maximal resoluteness. We shall review three important hypotheses.

It is of importance to point out in advance that it is evident that, in the absence of data, there should be three hypotheses. Since we have to deal with the question concerning the origin of lifeless material (A) and of life (B) and their reciprocal relation, there are logically three possibilities: they are irrevocable (A + B); A is derived from B; or B is derived from A.

The first hypothesis emanates from the view that the living and the lifeless have always existed alongside each other (A + B). Life is thus essentially different from lifeless matter. It is not created, but it is as old as the world, eventually eternal. With this conception there is thus no room for spontaneous generation in any form. It is a return to the core of the idea of Anaxagoras. It also means a rejection of mechanism, as we have encountered it in the mechanistic monism of Haeckel. And it is an adherence to vitalism, the idea that there is active in organisms an all or not immaterial power of life that cannot be traced back to the physical-chemical. We thus get a dualistic conception. This view was held by various investigators at the end of the previous century. They had an open eye for the fact that life upon this earth, initially, was impossible, in view of the high temperature. The only conceivable conclusion was that a single form of life landed on this earth from space where it occurred, all or not localized, as cosmozoa. Richter, Liebig and von Helmholtz thought that we had to view meteorites as the means of transportation. Arrhenius (1859-1927) defended the view that living germs reached the earth by being propelled by radiation pressure (hypothesis of panspermy). Research on meteorites and the results of modern astronomy have not produced data that argue in favor of this hypothesis.

The second supposition concerning the problem of origin posits that the lifeless is derived from the living (B ──➤ A). This is a speculative process of thinking which, as it were, reverses the old problem. This view was held already by Preyer in 1880. According to him the fluid globe, which the earth initially was, was alive—a living organism. When the earth began to cool off, various parts began to die successively and became stones, water and the like. They were, as it were, the nails and hairs of the original organism. Between these dying rests there remained finally the living remnants, which we call organisms.

Only recently a similar view was propagated by Adolf Meyer-Abich. The modern atomic-theory and quantum-mechanics, according to him, gives many arguments for the view that we consider the universe a universal organism. "Momentarily this means for us that, if this universe itself is a universal organism, the old problem of spontaneous generation of the organismal from the anorganismal, has ceased to exist, just as perpetual motion is no longer a possible problem. Yes, the proven impossibility of an abiogenesis can be taken as an experimental proof for the organismal nature of the world as a whole."[11]

It needs not to be demonstrated that this second solution has hardly any adherents at all. At the same time it shows clearly how the holistic worldview of these investigators had a definite influence upon their approach to science. In addition, it is only one step from the universal organism to pantheism. However, Adolph Meyer-Abich definitely does not wish to make this step.

The third supposition we meet among modern views about the origin of life, is that life does not differ essentially from lifeless matter and originated from it in the past (A ——→ B). This possibility signifies a continuation of the line of materialistic monism of the previous century. Nearly all modern writers who occupy themselves with this problem accept this point of view. Their line of thought comes down to the following—no living organism originated spontaneously. That is why we should drop the component "spontaneous." This also means that Haeckel's Monera-theory was much too simplistic. Rather, during millions of years, gradually, step by step, as the result of physical and chemical circumstances, various preliminary stadia of life have been traversed accidentally and according to the laws of nature till, at the extreme end, life at first resulted. These preliminary stadia are designated as pre-micro-organisms, molecular-bionts, eobionts and the like.[12]

In view of the great influence which this theory exercises upon modern biological thinking and also because of the significance which it has for our conclusions at the end of this chapter, we

---

[11] A. Meyer-Abich, *Acta Biotheorica* 7, p. 66, 1943. See especially his extensive study, *Naturphilosophie auf neuen Wegen*, 1948.

[12] See W. J. Alexander, *Life, Its Nature and Origin*, New York, 1948; W. A. Collier, ibid., 1949.

shall discuss this view somewhat more extensively than the preceding two.

There is a general opinion that upon this earth, originally, because of the high temperature, life was impossible. Life, accordingly must have originated upon this earth about a billion years ago.[13] Now, all life is dependent upon so-called organic substances, more or less complicated carbon-compounds, among which the proteins predominate in all organisms.

There is at the same time a general agreement that these organic substances originally were not present at all upon the earth. The first question that confronts us in this line of thought is thus concerning the origin of these organic substances, particularly the proteins. These must have originated from the substances which at that time were present in the water and in the atmosphere. Now, we are quite sure that in the atmosphere of many stars (among others, the sun) there are present hydrocarbons (compounds of carbon and hydrogen). It also has been demonstrated that in the atmosphere of the larger planets, such as Jupiter and Saturn, methane is present in great quantities; while, in addition, hydrocarbons have been found in meteorites. It is considered probable, therefore, that in the atmosphere of the earth, before life existed, there were present hydrocarbons, particularly methane. This opinion is strengthened by the fact that in volcanic eruptions metal-carbides come to the surface, which in combination with water-vapor form hydrocarbons. Further, it has been determined that in the atmosphere of several neighboring planets there are considerable quantities of ammonia. There is thus the general conviction that the atmosphere originally contained particularly methane, ammonia, water-vapor and hydrogen.

It is thus thought possible that from these components there originated the first organic matter. This view was completely hypothetical till a short time ago. But recently an important argument in its favor has been adduced through the experiments

---

[13] See for the methodology and for the more or less great certainty of the determination of the age of the earth: A. Knopf, "Time in Earth History," in: G. L. Jepsen, G. G. Simpson and E. Mayr, *Genetics, Paleontology and Evolution*, Princeton, 1949, p. 1-9; F. E. Zeuner, *Dating the Past*, 3rd ed., London, 1952. For an extensive discussion of this problem from the Christian point of view, see G. J. Sizoo and others, *De Ouderdom der Aarde*, 4th ed. Kampen, 1955, and H. R. Woltjer, "The Age of the Earth," *Free Univ. Quart.* 3, 188-204, 1955.

of the American Miller.[14] For a week he induced electrical discharges through a mixture of methane, ammonia, water-vapor and
hydrogen. This, as we saw, probably corresponded qualitatively
in composition with the atmosphere of the earth before the existence of life. After this operation he could demonstrate with
certainty that organic substances had originated, particularly
several amino acids. The amino acids are the "building stones"
of the proteins.

This experiment thus made it appear probable that in the original
atmosphere the building stones of the proteins could originate
through the influence of electrical discharges (lightning), but
possibly the same process could be effected by the ultra-violet
light of the sun.

It is supposed that these processes took place during a very long
period of time, with the result that the oceans gradually contained large quantities of amino acids. The next phase then must
have been that these amino acids became linked to one another,
thus forming protein-like compounds. This is indeed one of the
most difficult phases to explain because this reaction normally
takes place only under the influence of so-called enzymes and
these themselves are proteins occurring only in living beings.

Many have supposed that they could overcome this difficulty
through the following reasoning. It is known that enzymes are
not consumed by a reaction, but that they only hasten such a
reaction. Or, as Wald[15] says, "Every process that is catalysed
by an enzyme, and every product of such a process would occur
without the enzyme. The only difference is one of rate. Once
again the essence of the argument is time" (p. 48). It is said
further that, since there were millions of years available, the
process of the origin of proteins must have occurred frequently
simply because of the law of chance.

From the statistical side sharp criticism often has been leveled
against this line of thought. The most evident is perhaps the
following estimate of the German Schulz.[16] He handles the

---

[14]S. L. Miller, "A Production of Amino Acids under Possible Primitive Earth
Conditions," *Science*, 117, 528-529, 1953.

[15]Cf., e.g., G. Wald, "The Origin of Life," *Scientific American*, 191, 45-53,
1954.

[16]Schulz, according to Troll, *Das Virusproblem in ontologischer Sicht*, Wiesbaden, 1951; see also P. Lecomte du Nouy, *Human Destiny*, New York, 1947,
pp. 22-37; H. J. Jordan, *De Causale verklaring van het leven*, Amsterdam, 1940,
pp. 27-34.

question of how great the chance is that a protein molecule could have originated in such a fashion. What is the probability that from the free interplay of amino-acid molecules there originates a protein built up of 1000 amino acids in a definite arrangement as they always occur in normal proteins? It appears that by considering a great number of simplifications this probability amounts to 10^{-1360} if for instance 1000 kg. of amino acids gets the chance for this reaction during a billion years. This means thus a decimal fraction with 1359 zeros after the decimal point.

Schulz tries to give us an impression of this by means of two examples. He asks what is the chance that with one grasp in the Sahara desert we can catch a particular grain of sand. This chance appears to be about 10^{-24}. Even more illustrative is the answer to the question, what is the probability of catching a definite atom from all the atoms present in the universe. This chance appears to be but 10^{-80}. Hence Schulz comes to the conclusion that the chance that proteins originated in this fashion virtually can be put at zero.

Various investigators, mindful of the fact that living protoplasm is not built up out of proteins alone but also from hundreds of other substances, come to the conclusion that even because of this the idea of a pre-evolution is an absurdity. Other investigators perceive that in a watery solution of amino acids no proteins can originate, but they are convinced that there have been circumstances upon this earth under which this reaction indeed could take place. The Russian investigator Oparin has occupied himself with this problem for many years.[17] He pointed out only recently that they have succeeded in Russia, by using a pressure of several thousands of atmospheres, in linking together two or three amino acids in a mixture of amino acids, in the presence of an enzyme.[18] Although an enzyme was used here, Oparin is of the opinion that this experiment demonstrated that under high pressure protein-like substances can originate. He points out that similar high pressures are present in the depths of the oceans.

---

[17] A. I. Oparin, *The Origin of Life*, New York, 1938.

[18] A. I. Oparin, "Das Problem der Entstehung des Lebens im Lichte der modernen Naturwissenschaft," *Sowjetwissenschaft* (Naturw. Abt.), 7, p. 299-309, 1954.

We may conclude upon the basis of the preceding that it may be considered possible that various types of organic matter could originate upon the earth at the time when no life was present. On the other hand it is very problematical whether (and if it is thus, how) large molecules such as proteins could form.

Let us, for instance, accept that indeed proteins and similar compounds so originated. Then the question presents itself, how it is that these compounds could continue to exist, because we can observe at present that in nature there begins immediately a destruction of such molecules. And the breaking down would surely conquer the construction. However, when we today trace what causes this demolition, then there seem to be two factors: living organisms (bacteria and the like) and oxidation through oxygen. It speaks for itself that the first factor falls away because we are considering exactly the time when there were not any organisms. The second factor, oxygen, still remains. And there are many who think that initially there was present in the atmosphere of the earth no or only very little oxygen. This is a cardinal point. Wald says, for example: "If this were not so, it would be very difficult to imagine how organic matter could accumulate over the long stretches of time that alone might make possible the spontaneous origin of life."[19] Many are thus of the opinion that initially no free oxygen occurred. This means that the oceans were entirely sterile, while the breaking down processes of the organic compounds that had just originated were limited to a minimum. Also carbon dioxide must have been absent in the primitive atmosphere of the earth.

If this is correct then this is very interesting because it would mean that the two gases that today are indispensable for the life of higher plants and animals, in the course of time have been produced by the organisms themselves. When the continued existence of organic broth has to be attributed to the absence of oxygen and of living organisms, then this means also that an origin of life, as it is pictured here, could take place only during a very limited period of the history of the earth. The view that

---

[19]G. Wald, *op. cit.*, p. 49.

is propagated occasionally, that even today new life can originate on the earth, is also for that reason improbable.[20]

The difficulty of the destruction (of the protein molecules) is thus conquered, at least in theory. However, there is another obstacle, namely, that such reactions as those of the amino acids into protein-like substances are reversible—they go both ways. This difficulty can be overcome, however, if the product of the reaction is more stable. To prevent this difficulty it is pointed out that proteins have the tendency to form larger units, so-called aggregates. And when they have once been formed they can again organize within themselves, in the course of time, various other substances.

At this stage it is supposed that already phenomena have occurred that resembled life. 1. When the particles become too large they fall apart into a number of new particles that in turn can grow again (propagation). 2. One can consider that already then have originated enzymatic substances that could influence definite reactions (metabolism). 3. Through this some particles get the advantage over others, and there originates something like a "struggle for life," so that through "selection" the better "adapted" particles multiply themselves at the expense of the ones that are less adapted. When once it has gone that far, according to many, one can speak of a living organism. It is indeed still very primitive, yet it has the properties of reproduction, growth, metabolism and the like.

Of course, now arises the question about the food of these organisms. Naturally this cannot have been anything else than the great mass of organic substances that originated in the course of millions of years. From this the first living organisms came forth and when they once had come into existence, they began to consume gradually the nutrient broth. The only way in which this can happen without oxygen is through fermentation. Thus, by "inventing" fermentation-processes these organisms could continue to live. Of course, the quantity of food was limited. When the broth was entirely devoured the life that just had originated would have to die again. There thus came a critical stage. In addition, fermentation is a process that produces

---

[20] I. Lichtig. *Entstehung des Lebens durch stetige Schöpfung.* Amsterdam, 1938.

only relatively little energy, so that life only just remained. With the fermentation-process, however, carbon dioxide originates. Thus, during this period of the history of the earth there was formed by the first living organisms the carbon dioxide that is still present in the atmosphere. And before the nutrient broth was entirely consumed, there originated "by chance" in the organisms complicated compounds whereby they were enabled to assimilate the carbon dioxide that they had fabricated before; the process of photosynthesis originated whereby the organisms by means of sunlight could make new organic compounds through carbon dioxide. They could thus themselves fabricate organic substances in the future and were not dependent upon the exhaustible quantity that originated at previous times. These substances they could then again ferment.

We have seen already that by these fermentation processes only a little energy is liberated. There occurred, however, after a long period of time a happy circumstance. With photosynthetic processes oxygen is liberated. The atmosphere of the earth thus gradually became very rich in oxygen. The happy chance was that in the organisms now originated enzymes that made it possible to derive with the aid of oxygen much more energy from the substances that arose by photosynthesis. Respiration thus had its origin. This "invention" signified a tremendous step in the right direction, because the abundant energy gained in this fashion opened the way for the development of many new substances and processes. Only then could evolution have a good beginning.

According to Wald,[21] something was added to this. Initially life was possible only in water because this absorbed the fierce ultra-violet rays of the light of the sun that could penetrate the atmosphere. However, when once a large quantity of oxygen had accumulated, a layer of ozone was formed in the upper atmosphere which performed the same function of absorption. When this ozone layer once had come into existence and respiration had been "invented," only then did life become possible on the land and in the air. From now on the organisms could leave the water.

[21] G. Wald. op. cit., p. 53.

The preceding reasoning, in which the high points of a number of modern conceptions are given in resume without entering into questions of detail, makes it clear that today we can speak much more concretely about the origin of life than in the times of Haeckel. His whole line of thought proceeded from his materialistic-monistic worldview. Today the background is still the same but advanced research has produced much material that makes scientific discussion possible.

Notwithstanding this indispensable advance, we should keep in mind that all these views are practically entirely hypothetical and are only a scientific game invented by those who have accepted this worldview as their faith. For example, we are not sure that the earth originated as a red-hot globe from the sun, because during recent years the view becomes more and more predominant that our planet originated "cold," from interstellar material.[22] The point of view is also defended by some that it is not methane, but carbon dioxide that has been the source of the carbon of the organic compounds. At the same time others suppose that in the first origin of life oxidative reactions with oxygen have been the determining factors.[23] Still others consider the possibility that life originated not gradually but suddenly by chance,[24] through very unexpected processes; moreover the opinion is expressed that not proteins but nucleic acids were the first organic complexes.[25]

In reviewing the literature one comes to the conclusion that there are about as many hypotheses as there are authors. And one enjoys their ingenuity in first posing definite problems and then conquering or avoiding them with clever reasoning, but one gets the impression that he is not acquiring knowledge about what actually happened a billion years ago.

We have followed in the preceding pages the history of the spontaneous generation idea through the centuries of western

[22]See, e.g., J. Bernal. "The Origin of Life," *New Biology*, 16, pp. 28-40. 1954; see also his book: *The Physical Basis of Life*, London, 1952.

[23]J. W. S. Pringle, "The Evolution of Living Matter," *New Biology*, 16, pp. 54-67, 1954.

[24]N. W. Pirie, "On Making and Recognizing Life," *New Biology*, 16, pp. 41-53, 1954.

[25] H. J. Muller, "Life," *Science*, 121, 1-9, 1955.

thought. With that it has become evident to us that successively various worldviews have dominated the natural-scientific hold on this problem. We saw that the Greek, Christian, materialistic and other spheres of faith found their repercussion in the domain of practical fieldwork, microscopy, biochemistry and other scientific categories that usually assert that they occupy themselves only with facts. Portmann's picture seems correct in every respect.

As a result of thousands of years of thinking and experimenting, modern science presents us with three speculations about the origin of life: 1) the principle of life is as old as matter; 2) initially all matter was alive; 3) life came from lifeless matter. The question which naturally presents itself to us is whether we should not conclude that the one view is more scientific than the other. Is there not one, among all these views, that can be designated as purely scientific—these views varying as they do from Naegeli's well-known expression, "Die Urzeugung leugnen heiszt das Wunder verkünden" (to deny abiogenesis means to declare a miracle) to von Bertalanffy's "Satz der unmöglichen Urzeugung"[26] (the dogma of impossible abiogenesis)? This question is of great importance to us.

In our search for an answer we wish to direct our attention first of all to the established data, according to our present knowledge, which have been obtained after thousands of years. They are the following:

1. None of the recent organisms can originate spontaneously from lifeless matter.

2. None of organisms of which we have found fossil remains came into existence spontaneously from lifeless matter.

3. Life appeared on the earth between one or two billion years ago.

4. The oldest fossils that we know are of algae or bacteria.

If one wants to be *purely scientific* in his judgment then he should leave it at that. One thus comes to the conclusion that we *factually know nothing* about the origin of life. If then one wishes to labor with this problem in a purely scientific way, then

---

[26] L. von Bertalanffy, *Theoretische Biologie I*, Berlin 1932, p. 130 ff.

one can, for example, carry out analyses of the oldest rocks. Possibly that will give us additional data.

Every line of thought that goes beyond that and pretends to know more is no longer purely scientific, but has its origin in a philosophy, a worldview or in a religion.

The vitalistic and holistic[27] biologists for the most part are willing to admit this, but the mechanists often consider that they alone have the right to the title of being scientific. And surely, in the specific instance of this problem, their opinion has advantages over other views. It also has to be admitted that this view is the most attractive for those who have received their biological training during the twentieth century. Indeed, with the aid of a speculative but yet scientific-like complex of hypotheses, the transition from the lifeless to the living is thus made to sound logical. We have to think of the fact, however, that this view has inextricable consequences in which the essential point often comes to the fore more clearly: that living matter is not qualitatively different from the lifeless, but that also, for instance, man is not essentially different from the animal; all human capacities have evolved from animal characters. The only insoluble problem in this reasoning is the riddle about the origin of the universe. When the first germ of it once had originated, the rest developed only through the influence of purely physicochemical laws. No one can deny that the factual data give no impetus to this line of reasoning and that the cardinal questions, which to a large extent still have to be solved, are eliminated *a priori* in this way. Although this opinion is attractive from the point of view of natural science, and appears simple, in its origin it is of a purely philosophic nature. Since most followers of this opinion think it is inherent in their point of view to render judgment about the all or none existence of God, and to call themselves atheistic, pantheistic or deistic, or to be such in fact, it

---

[27] Holistic and holism are derived from the Greek holos. It has reference to the philosophical theory that the main factor governing the course of evolution is an impulse toward construction of wholes. The author of both name and theory was Jan Christian Smuts (1870-1950). He maintained that even in inorganic matter there is a tendency to form patterns or wholes. In his *Holism and Evolution* (1926) he points out that it may be seen in the structure of the atom, chemical compounds and more clearly in the cell. As applied to biology the theory has striking parallels to the *Gestalt* theory in psychology. —(Translator's note)

appears that the religious element occupies a central and aprioristic place in their thinking.

6. *Creationism and the Problem of the Origin of Life*

The last question which we should pose in this chapter is how we as Christians define our position in regard to this problem. We shall formulate our provisional answer upon the basis of the conclusions of the first chapter. (In the last chapter only can we come to a more definite view.)

We begin by stating in advance that the scientific data, as formulated on page 52, are accepted by us with the restriction "according to our present knowledge." We thus have this in common with all other investigators. But to what extent does our *faith* exercise influence upon our scientific thinking regarding the origin of life? As we saw earlier, we can reduce this question to the problem of what Scripture tells us about the origin of life. We find that Genesis 1:11, 12 tells us: "And God said, Let the earth put forth grass, herbs yielding seed, *and* fruit-trees bearing fruit after their kind, wherein is the seed thereof, upon the earth; and it was so. And the earth brought forth grass, herbs yielding seed after their kind, and trees bearing fruit, wherein is the seed thereof, after their kind: and God saw that it was good."

And verses 20 and 21: "And God said, Let the waters swarm with living creatures, and let the birds fly above the earth in the open firmament of heaven. And God created the great seamonsters, and every living creature that moveth, wherewith the waters swarmed, after their kind, and every winged bird after its kind: and God saw that it was good."

And verses 24 and 25: "And God said, Let the earth bring forth living creatures after their kind, cattle and creeping things, and beasts of the earth after their kind: and it was so. And God made the beasts of the earth after their kind, and the cattle after their kind, and everything that creepeth upon the ground after its kind: and God saw that it was good."

Let us first take the position of fundamentalism still so prevalent, that we must bring the texts of Genesis into contact with our scientifically ascertainable reality. Then one usually comes to the conclusion that it says plainly in Genesis 1 that God created the herbs, the fruit trees, the large and small sea animals, cattle, birds and others according to the constancy of their species, in this sense that God, out of nothing, placed them entire and mature upon the earth and in the water. This is the idea of "special creations," which, it is said, we meet even today.

Placing ourselves for a moment in this line of thought, we must begin by pointing out that this presentation of affairs is not taught in Genesis. The creating out of nothing is an addition, a concoction, because the direct relation with what already existed concretely is emphasized *more* in Genesis 1 than "special creations," when, among others, it is recorded that *the earth brought forth* grass.

Already in 1899 Dr. A. Kuyper pointed to this. He says: ". . . the creation document of Scripture rather eliminates than recommends the *dramatic* appearance of new beings. It says that *'the earth brought forth* cattle and creeping things,' not that God placed them upon the earth like pieces on a chessboard."[28] The fundamentalist line of thought must teach, if it wishes to be consistent, that the living organisms came forth out of the earth. This signifies in fact, if taken literally, not much else than a *"generatio spontanea."* And we have pointed out that early Christian thinkers like Augustine in those times drew this conclusion from the texts cited; in this sense, that they accepted that initially concrete germs of life were created, which partly came to development very soon at the command of God, but while other parts became living beings only at a later date. We also saw that this view originated through an adaptation of the Christian faith to the data of natural science.

In the following chapter we shall see that many groups of organisms in the plant and animal world appeared successively upon the earth. This presents a great stumbling block for fundamentalism, since here again only an adaptation can furnish the solution, namely, the postulation that concrete germs of these groups were initially created in order to unfold themselves later. If one rejects this then one has to accept the evolutionary thought that the newly appearing forms descended from the ones that already existed. This, however, would be in conflict with the view of the constancy of kinds.

---

[28] A. Kuyper. *Evolutie*, Amsterdam, 1899.

We should realize also, however, that the thought of such concrete germs is a fabrication. The text says literally that the earth brought forth. This means that fundamentalism really cannot lodge an objection against the principle of the materialistic conception which we expounded a few pages back. That they do not draw this self-evident conclusion probably must be attributed to attachment to the science of a few centuries ago, when it became evident that the spontaneous generation idea, which had been defended for centuries with Bible-texts, was completely unfounded. When now in principle the same idea is being propagated as an essential part of evolutionism, they recoil from the consequences in two directions.

As we indicated in our first chapter, fundamentalism constantly leads to such contradictions and thus raises one problem after another. In reference to that we remarked that Scripture does not impart to us scientific data, but only realities that cannot be discovered through scientific investigation. This means that with the problem of the origin of life, the texts we quoted teach us that it was God at whose command (*God said*) and according to whose will the entity of life has been created and organisms have come into existence. He determined that they should exist and how (after their kind) they should come into existence. They do not contain an eternal principle and not one of them issues from God, but they originate immanently (let the earth bring forth) within the creation. These communications guide the faith of the Christian and determine his worldview. The idea that organisms could have come into existence concretely *only* through accidental chance-processes that could have run all or not in a different fashion, is thus for us not acceptable. The origin of organisms occurred intentionally and ran its course according to a plan, even though from a scientific point of view we can record only chance-processes.

These actualities are thus *revealed* to us in Genesis, since we are not able to discover them through research; for when we start to investigate, we are even inclined to interpret them just the other way.

When we see that this is the message in the texts cited, then we notice to our amazement that we are not told at all how the organisms came into concrete existence, indeed not even in which way. It does not say that God created them out of nothing, nor that God at that time created the power or powers of life, nor that there was a pre-evolution, or that definite organisms could originate or not from other organisms. In short, it says nothing about what we could call scientific data. About the concrete origin of organisms no factual communications are furnished to us.

This means that our minds are open to the few data science has found and at the same time that within the framework of revealed realities we are free to investigate this problem and to develop our thoughts.

Naturally, our faith that the entity of life "has been created" is in direct contradiction with the view that this could have come into existence *only* through the zigzag game of physical-chemical happenings fortuitously from lifeless matter, as only a quantitative variation from it; *"creatio" i*n the absolute sense stands over against *"evolutio"* in the absolute sense. But to point out *where* and *when* life appeared for the first time, *how* this process came about and *what* originated in that way, is impossible. The Christian biologist will thus take the position that God brought life into existence under the care of his guidance.

In that regard we find in present-day Christian thinking three possibilities:

1. primary life is created out of nothing;
2. a vital element has been introduced in a definite material construction through which this became alive;
3. the essence of the entity of life in the organisms consists in its specific structure which was created "in the beginning." It is being realized constantly under God's guidance, along a line of (for us possibly improbable, but rightly) natural processes, since this entity of life was present in creation as possibility (we could also say, as necessity).

Which of these three possibilities is the right one we cannot prove by the method of *natural science,* if we take into consideration the paucity of our knowledge and the lack of insight concerning the structure of recent living organisms. The third suggested possibility, to which we give preference (see our last chapter), shows ostensibly much similarity with the materialistic approach to the problem. Hence we give the following supplement. Suppose that later on this idea appeared to be correct, that life made its appearance via amino acids, proteins, aggregates and the like; then the Christian will view it as follows. He believes that God created nature in the beginning in a very special way with a definite number of very specific elements which possess special attributes and with the mandate and the potentiality that specific entities would develop later (they are thus laid in the created totality at creation). Then God caused to exist such a state of affairs of moisture, pressure, temperature and the like, that all conditions for the realization of life as he wished it had been fulfilled. Then there came a sequence of processes (in their appearance and in this succession for us perhaps statistically improbable) according to the laws laid down in nature at the dawn of creation. Through these processes, step by step, and very purposefully, the atoms and molecules were arranged and combined so that there originated a very definitely constructed protoplasm in which the created entity of life became manifested.

From the positing of these possibilities alone it appears that Christianity has no doctrinaire pretensions that it knows *how* primitive life came into existence, but only that it finds its origin in being created by God. Christianity thus defends in the scientific discussion about this problem that the idea of *absolute* autonomic laws is out of the question; that no *chance* in the old-fashioned sense, but of which one still hears very often, dominated the processes which eventually produced this life; that it has been willed *thus* purposefully and specifically.

That the Christian biologist leaves the *how* undecided, is an indication that he does not have to introduce in the problematics of natural science a *deus ex machina,* as is often asserted; but that he as a scientist can assume an even freer position over against these problems than, for example, the doctrinaire mechanist whose philosophy forces him to speculate, since his worldview stands or falls with a definite solution to this problem.

The Christian knows that all entities of reality were created in the beginning. Along which road these entities came to realization is a problem for science.

CHAPTER THREE

THE ORIGIN OF THE TYPES OF ORGANISMS

1. *Introduction*

In the preceding chapter we discussed the problem of the origin of life. We established first of all that in the course of the history of western science this problem was stated in a more and more abstract form. First the question was applied to frogs and mice. After that attention was focused respectively upon one-celled organisms, Monera and viruses, to culminate at last in a discussion about "life" itself.

We next established that the current explanations for the origin of life are very hypothetical and are based upon more or less acceptable views rather than upon established data.

Now life upon this earth, at any rate at present, does not exist as such, but is found only in *living organisms*. The next question which we thus have to face is that concerning the origin of organisms. How did organisms appear on the earth in the past and in what did their mutual relation consist?

Before we can go into the discussion of this question we must make the following remarks:

a.   It is plain that true knowledge about what has happened in the past can be obtained only from records of the past. Our planet has been made in such a way that such records have been preserved in it, in the form of fossils, mostly petrified remnants of plants and animals that lived in former ages. We should attribute much value to what these fossils teach us.

b.   In the second place, it should be pointed out that the realm of organisms can be divided into groups. The largest groups are called phyla (e.g., Protozoa, Annelida, Arthropoda, Echinodermata); the smallest groups are called species (*e.g.,* domestic cats). Between these two group-ideas there are to be distinguished a whole series of other categories, *e.g.* :

Phylum	Chordata (animals with a special kind of axial skeleton)
Subphylum	Vertebrata (animals with a spinal column)
Class	Mammalia (mammals)
Order	Carnivora (flesh eating mammals, including cats, dogs, bears, and the like)
Family	Felidae (cat-like animals)
Genus	Felis (cats)
Species	Felis domestica (domestic cats)

In this chapter we shall occupy ourselves mainly with the higher categories, while the following chapter is devoted to the species.

2.   *History Concerning the Problem of the Origin of Organisms*
We have seen how the Greeks and the thinkers of the Middle Ages had the idea that all kinds of organisms could originate from matter. It is no wonder that when the boundary between the lifeless and the living thus faded, the boundaries between the types of organisms also became hazy in practice.

Thus Albertus Magnus (1206-1280) gives a few examples from which it appears, according to his opinion, that one type of plant can change into another. This can happen through the transformation of the seed: rye can change into wheat and vice versa. According to him this transformation occurs every three years. Also from the decaying remnants of one plant another can originate: after the chopping down of an oak and a beech forest there originates an aspen or a birch forest. Once it was even "observed" that when a branch of an oak had been stuck into the ground grape-vines grew out of it. It also was established definitely in his mind that from a diseased tree parasites can originate.[1] During the Middle Ages there were many scholars that were convinced that there is in nature a large measure of variability and that organisms are not at all constant in their structure. The question of origin they explained through divine creation, but the organisms were thought to be much more plastic than we see them today.

From this we can learn that there was a time in which, even though Christian thinking predominated, there was not a single objection against the view that one form of plant or animal could transform into another. This opinion was embraced even more extensively when the marine merchants brought with them from new continents the strangest exotic plants and animals. The museums filled with them suggested that the abundance of forms was infinitely great and that plants and animals could exchange their characteristics without limit. This was the time of sea-monsters and mermaids, the time in which it was thought that ducks and geese originated from the still so-called goose-barnacles, scorpions from rooster-eggs, and that in 1553 a woman had given birth to a frog with the tail of a serpent.[2]

In the 17th century a reaction set in because of the influence of physics and chemistry. These sciences discovered that matter is bound by fixed laws; that one cannot in a mysterious way change lead and other base metals into silver or gold, and that ice does not change into quartz, as had been thought for a long time. The Philosopher's Stone of the alchemists gradually lost in interest. Instead there began to predominate in science observation, detailed description, verification and experimentation. Thus investigators of nature developed the firm conviction that nature is not a hazy chaos, but that it is built out of a definite number of elements and that relations among these elements are not variable but constant;

---

[1] E. Radl, *Geschichte der biologischen Theorien in der Neuzeit I*, Leipzig, 1913, p. 264.

[2] R. E. D. Clark, *Darwin: Before and After*, London, 1948, Grand Rapids, 1958, p. 37.

that the elements possess characteristics that can be sharply circumscribed and that they react according to fixed laws.

In imitation of this there also occurred a shift in biology. The
idea of a continuous coming into existence of new life from lifeless matter, which had been embraced for ages, the idea of spontaneous generation, lost ground. The stories of monsters and
mermaids appeared to be pure fantasy. The number of plant
and animal forms appeared limited. Organisms could not transform into one another. Thus the thinking of the biologists took
an entirely different direction. They began to view the possibility
of systematic arrangement of organisms. The primitive museums,
filled to overflowing with strange and rare specimens, where the
jaws of the whale hung next to the teeth of the elephant and
lobsters next to the calabashes, veritably begged for systematic
arrangement. As a primary result of these changed conditions,
systematic biology acquired its great pioneers, culminating in the
Swedish investigator Carolus Linnaeus (1707-1778), who wrote
his *Systema Naturae* in the Netherlands in 1735. In this he
assigned a place to virtually all the organisms known at that time
in the plant and animal worlds.

In the preceding we have pictured in bold strokes the course of
practical biology. In addition to this, however, over a long period
of time, theoretical thinking dwelt upon the question concerning the
relation of organisms. Passing by many important thinkers (in
the following chapter we will return to this more extensively), we
wish to stop and consider the philosophy of Leibniz (1646-1716)
who had a great influence upon Linnaeus, but especially upon the
theoretical biology that came after him. Through the peculiar
construction of his so-called monadology,[3] Leibniz not only laid
the basis for the later evolutionistic principle of continuity in
biology, but also that of the principle of constancy which was of
such importance in biology at the beginning of the last century.

Leibniz held the view that reality is constituted of an infinite
number of infinitesimally small substances or monads. These
are completely enclosed within themselves and cannot directly
affect one another. They are "windowless"; however, they have

[3]G. W. Leibniz, *Hauptschriften zur Grundlegung der Philosophie, II*, pp.
435-456, Philosophische Bibliothek, Bd. 108, Leipzig, 1906.

"perceptions" in which the whole universe is mirrored. Through a so-called *"harmonia praestabilita"* (pre-established harmony) all these perceptions are held in strict harmony with one another. The monads differ only in the degree of clearness of their inner perceptions. And now, in accordance with the principle of continuity, the *"lex continui"* as Leibniz discovered it in mathematics, the perceptions of the monads are arranged in a continuous series of degrees of clarity, while transitions between two successive monads are infinitesimally small. The monads are thus placed in a continuous ascending order which exhibits the following steps:

1. the unknowing and unconscious material monads;
2. the unknowing conscious monads (of living organisms);
3. the knowing conscious monads, or human soul monads which are still confined to the material monads of the body;
4. the purely spiritual monads (spirits, angels), culminating in the divine as central monad, whose thinking is creating at the same time.

In this fashion there were arranged, in a hierarchal ascending ladder, lifeless matter, plants, animals, man, spirits, angels and God, whereby through the assumption of infinitesimally small transitions, the boundaries were erased. This world-presupposition of Leibniz had two mutually contradictory central ideas that have been of great importance for later biology:

a. In the first place, the monads are fixed immutable entities that have been created by God, so-called *"vérités éternelles"*, "eternal ideas of creation."

b. But, in the second place, the monads have been placed in a gradual arrangement so that in the process of thinking they may be deducted from one another, the *"lex continui."*

Thus, on the one hand, a fixed constancy; on the other hand, a logical mathematical continuity. From the latter, viewed in the light of the former, we cannot conclude that Leibniz was an evolutionist. "His stepladder presents only a next-to-one-another, not an out-of-one-another."[4]

Hence, according to Leibniz, the groups of organisms, even the species, were constant. Sometimes he expresses himself in an evolutionistic way, as in the following: "It is possible that at

---

[4] Uhlmann, E. *Entwicklungsgedanke und Artbegriff*, Jena, 1923, p. 21.

sometime or somewhere in the universe the species of animals were or are subject to change more than is the case among us, and that many animals which have something of the cat in them, as the lion, the tiger and the lynx, must have been of one race and could pass, as it were, as subdivisions of the old "species of cat." Thus I come back again to this, as I have said so many times, that our determinations of the natural species are provisional and correspond with our knowledge."[5] When Leibniz expresses himself in such fashion, he has in mind the relation of this to his whole theory in which the real discontinuity of the *"vérités éternelles"* remains at the opposite pole of his *"lex continui."*

This appears, for example, from his statement: "If we had the penetrating sharp vision of a higher spirit and could pierce through this matter deeply enough, we probably would find fixed attributes for every species, which are common in all their individuals and are ever present as fixed in the same organism, no matter what change or transformation they may experience."[6]

Leibniz has thus been of great importance for the history of biology because in his monadology there are brought together the old view of ideas of creation as found among the Greeks as well as the church fathers (*e.g.,* Augustine), and which for a long time had a predominating influence in the thinking of scientists; while alongside of this the factor of the *"lex continui"* opened the way for evolutionism. We shall see how both central ideas have led to important trends in biology.

The first line of thought, that of constancy, leads from Leibniz to Linnaeus and from him through Cuvier to the so-called idealistic morphology. When Uhlmann discusses Linnaeus, he remarks: "a definite dependence on the part of Linnaeus in his theory of knowledge upon the ideology of Plato, by way of Leibniz, is unmistakable."[7] Linnaeus tried to apprehend the *natural system* of organisms as instituted at the time of creation.

Also with the noted French zoologist George Cuvier (1769-1832) we find the ideal of this (constant) natural system. Through this he became the great continuer of the work of Linnaeus. By

---

[5] Quoted after Radl. *op. cit.*, p. 222.
[6] Quoted after Uhlmann, *op. cit.*, p. 22
[7] Uhlmann, *op. cit.*, p. 19.

directing to that end his anatomical investigations, as he searched for the chief groups in the animal kingdom, he came to the following conclusion:

"If one considers the animal kingdom according to the principles which we described, and we clear away established prejudices about formerly supposed divisions and regard only the organization and nature of the animals and not their size and usefulness, nor the degree of knowledge we have about them, nor all the other minor circumstances, one finds that there exist four principle types, four general plans, so to say, after which all the animals seem to have been modeled. The subsequent divisions of these types, notwithstanding the terms with which they have been dignified by the naturalists, are only modifications of a minor character, based upon development or upon addition of some parts which do not change the plan essentially."[8]

These four groups are:

> Vertebrata (fish, amphibians, reptiles, birds, mammals);
> Articulata (e.g., lobsters and insects);
> Mollusca (e.g., snails and squids);
> Radiata (e.g., corals and jelly-fish).

These four groups he considered mutually irreducible animal kingdoms, and independent from one another, created thus by God. His whole theoretical biology was based upon the idea of absolute constancy. The philosophical continuity-idea of Leibniz had not influenced him. That is why many of his contemporaries considered his ideas old-fashioned. Cuvier, from his side, could reproach them for being influenced by the German philosophy of nature.

Especially through this idea of the *"plan général,"* Cuvier was the precursor of the so-called *idealistic morphology* or *typology.* That which distinguishes Cuvier from the later morphologists was his conception of the aim of comparative anatomy. To him it meant the study of the different organs in relation to their function. Through this his comparative anatomy acquired a trend in the direction of physiology and the emphasis is thus not upon pure form. The real founder of idealistic morphology was

---

[8] G. Cuvier, *Le règne animal; Les mammifères,* Paris, 1828, p. 54.

Vicq d'Azyr (1748-1794). He and his followers no longer viewed the differences in the structure of animals as expression of purposeful, physiological functions, as the object of morphology. They placed the emphasis upon similarity in all the different animals. Pure form became the object of study and all side-issues were rejected. Thus true *morphology* was born (the term owes its origin to Goethe).

For Vicq d'Azyr, for example, it was a problem how it is possible that a small part of the bottom of the human ocular orbit is formed by an extension of the maxillary bone since it would have been much simpler if the entire orbital wall had been formed out of one bone. It is plain that by positing such problems there was an attempt to penetrate to the orderly arrangement of animal structure. The answer to such questions is given by Vicq d'Azyr and, in him, by the entire idealistic morphology, by stating that there is revealed to us by all these forms that nature is always constructed according to some definite design. Thus we can distinguish in nature archetypes of which traces are found in all individuals which can be deduced from such an archetype.

The successor of the work of Vicq d'Azyr was Geoffroy St. Hilaire (1772-1844). He also looked for archetypes. From him originated the well-known statement that from the showcases of his bird collections the innumerably repeated type *"bird"* stared at him. He thus is the composer of the concept *"unité de plan"* ("The unity of the systems in the composition and the arrangement of the organic parts").

By this he means, according to the description of Lubosch, "that for him the unity existed in the constant return to the same position of all parts in relation to one another, which is entirely independent from the special functional form of the parts in each individual."[9] Lubosch adds to this, and that is interesting, when we look at what has just been said, "This was, as he says himself, initially a pure intuitive knowledge; later he found support in Leibniz' definition of the universe as a 'unity in multiformity,' in order to give his theory a broader foundation."[9]

The essence of Geoffroy's opinion is that in groups that be-

---

[9] W. Lubosch, in *Handbuch der vergleichenden Anatomie der Wirbeltiere I*, Berlin, 1931, p. 19.

long to a definite type all the individuals possess the same parts, since the higher plan of architecture is the same. One can thus never speak of the transformation from simple to the complex (also here a return to Leibniz).

Geoffroy teaches fundamentally the indivisibility of the animal kingdom, but not based upon the process of descent. This differentiates him from the earlier systematists (e.g., Cuvier, who differentiated four animal kingdoms), who regarded the animal kingdom as a multiplicity of irreducible units; and from the evolutionists because they rested the indivisibility upon a genetic basis. Thus he directed his attention again to the apparent deviations. The gills of fish formerly were viewed as something wholly peculiar to fish. Geoffroy brought them entirely within the type of vertebrates by demonstrating that equivalent structures occurred among the other vertebrates.

Here follow two examples of the morphological laws which this new science formulated:

1. the *"loi des connections"* (the law of connection): with different animals within one type, the parts of the organs, and the organs in distinction from one another, always occupy the same place: an organ is sooner transformed, reduced, or entirely omitted, than transposed.

2. the *"loi des balancements"* (the law of balance): every increase or change in an organ is always at the expense of another: the infinite variety of forms within a type in nature is based upon repeatedly other combinations of the proportions of organs.

Thus Geoffroy came to the idea of *metamorphosis*: the change within the architectural scheme, the change of form and function upon the basis of a typical structure. This metamorphosis is not a real transformation, but a thought-process.

This idealistic philosophy or typology is thus based upon the idea of constancy, which it attaches to the "type" - concept, the *"plan général"* of Cuvier. They searched for the unity among multiformity. They searched for "the vertebrate animal," "the bird," "the mollusc." Such a "type" as the greatest common denominator of the group-attributes, they also called (ideally) *primitive form,* archetype, without attaching to this word a concrete historical meaning. One can, for example, propose a primitive form, a type "vertebrate," by creating in one's thinking an animal which possesses all the common attributes of vertebrates (as fish, amphibians and the like). Such an animal, for example, may have a skull constructed of bony parts that regularly occur in all these animals, encasing the brain, and where one should differentiate the various parts common in all these animals. In addition, the head of this type should comprise the familiar cranial nerves, the paired eyes, nostrils, ears and mouth. The body would consist of the head, trunk (with the extremities bilaterally) and the tail. We thus see how one can reproduce the observed corresponding structures as it were in a pattern, a "type." The individual concrete animals which have been constructed according to this type we can derive from this type after a process of thinking, "metamorphosis," by placing individual animals in a "morphological series."

At this time we shall not venture further into the field of other concepts that have been important for this idealistic morphology (such as morphological homology and analogy) and of the structural laws that have been discovered by it. The significance of this science is plain. It was the biology of constancy which, upon the basis of its fundamental concepts of "type" and "morphological series," could name and explain all phenomena within morphology. In later years the essential idea was added to it that every type also has its own typical embryological development through which every animal that can be derived from such a type has to pass.

This attachment to the idea of constancy was easy as long as only the recent flora and fauna were known. However, at the beginning of the previous century there were found more and more fossils of plants and animals which differed often to a large extent in structure from the organisms of today. As we saw, they were first viewed as freaks of nature or as remnants of the models that God made in stone before he created living beings. Soon these opinions had to make way for the view that they are fossilized remnants of organisms that have long since ceased to exist. With this was born the problem of how to harmonize the constancy of recent flora and fauna with the earlier organisms which often differed from them markedly in structure.

Also here it was Cuvier, himself a great paleontologist, who gave a solution which was accepted quite generally for a long time. He held the view that during the history of the earth there have been a number of radical disasters of nature—catastrophes. Of these the Deluge was the last, whereby virtually all organisms perished and became fossils. After such a catastrophe the earth became peopled again with creatures issuing from the few organisms that had escaped. This meant that after such a catastrophe the flora and fauna that arose were only apparently new. The organisms that composed them had lived at an earlier period, but in such small numbers that they had not fossilized sooner. The followers of Cuvier modified his theory in this sense, that they accepted the view that with similar catastrophes all plants and animals perished and that God later created entirely new organisms.

Advanced research, however, made it necessary to make the number of catastrophes so large (some differentiated hundreds)[10] that one could not speak any more, in a single respect, of a satisfactory explanation.

At about the same time that idealistic morphology tried to explain the world of living organisms, proceeding from the idea of constancy, a morphology arose which tried to proceed from the entirely opposite evolutionary idea. Just as with the question about the origin of life, the Frenchman Lamarck here again was the pioneer. With him we find for the first time the *"lex continui"* consistently historically transferred into biology with the denial of the *"vérités éternelles."* This happened by way of Bonnet, of whom it is known that he was a devotee of the philosophy of Leibniz. Lamarck says somewhere in his *Philosophie Zoologique* : "For a long time it was thought that there exists a kind of ladder or a progressive chain among the living organisms. This view has been developed by Bonnet."[11]

By denying the constancy of the *"vérités éternelles"* he could

---

[10]Letter of Lyell to Darwin, Oct. 3, 1859. *Life and Letters of Charles Darwin, II,* p. 208.
[11] Lamarck, *op. cit.*, p. XXXV.

make the *"lex continui"* a principle for the descent of types. The *"lex continui"* became the "law of evolution," a principle according to which the groups of the animal kingdom can be placed in a series of descent. The arguments which Lamarck could adduce were few in number because only a limited quantity of fossils were known.

We should realize fully that this theory of evolution, in distinction from other biological theories, did not come into existence by way of induction, but that it arose through human thinking which turned away from the opinion that living organisms came into existence through creative acts of God.

Lamarck expresses himself as follows: "Shall I admire the greatness of the power of this first cause of everything any the less if it has pleased him that things should be thus, than if his will had occupied itself by separate acts and still continued to occupy itself with the details of all the special creations, variations, developments and perfections, destructions and renewals—in short, with all the mutations which take place at large among the things that exist?"[12]

From this it appears that his point of view approached that of deism, the thought of a First Cause.

Concerning the relation of the groups of organisms, he comes to the following point of view, reminiscent of Leibniz: "It may be truly said that there exist in each kingdom of living bodies groups that are arranged in single and graduated series, in conformity with the increasing complexity and arrangement of objects according to the account of reports. This series in the animal and vegetable kingdoms should contain at its anterior extremity, the simplest and the least organized living bodies and should end with those whose organization and faculties are most perfect."[13]

This repeated reference to the *"lex continui"* leads him to the conclusion: "This well recognized fact may furnish us with the greatest amount of light about the very order which nature followed in the production of all the animals which she has made to exist. . . ."[14] The first groups of animals which originated through

---

[12] Lamarck, *op. cit.*, pp. 48-49.   ,
[13] Lamarck, *op. cit.*, p. 88.
[14] Lamarck, *op. cit.*, p. 186.

spontaneous generation were the Infusoria and the worms. From these the animal kingdom developed in two directions. The line of the worms advanced by way of the molluscs to the vertebrates, to which also man belongs.—The line of the Infusoria leads, for example, to sponges, hydroids, jelly-fishes and corals.

The changed theoretical arrangement of Lamarck had a great influence upon his systematics. Let us cite one example of this. By his contemporaries, and also by Linnaeus, the mammals were called animals of the first grade because they resembled man. Lamarck, on the contrary, called the Infusoria, which originated through spontaneous generation, animals of the first grade, while the mammals (which appeared last) were counted as the last grade. The polarity of the systematics was thus changed. We see here clearly illustrated how in Lamarck's practical biology his theoretical system (if one wishes, his philosophical and his religious views) played a predominating role.

The process of "historicizing" morphology was not accelerated appreciably by Darwin (1809-1882), who was not a great theorist, so that we do not have to discuss his views here. It was Ernst Haeckel (1834-1919) who climaxed all this work. With him we find the central ideas of idealistic morphology transposed into a phylogenetic morphology, a doctrine of form that started from the principle of evolution.

The typical embryological development which we mentioned and which, according to idealistic morphology, is peculiar to each type, was the first item that was interpreted differently. The phenomenon that every mammal passes through a stage during which, superficially considered, gill-like organs are present, Haeckel viewed as "one of the most important and irrefutable proofs," *"einen der wichtigsten und unwiderleglichsten,"* for the theory of descent, and thus also for the historical derivation of types. He has defined this in his well-known biogenetic law: "ontogeny repeats phylogeny" ("die Ontogenie ist eine Rekapitulation der Phylogenie"), the embryological development is a repetition of the evolution. We should realize well that this thesis proceeded from a new worldview and that biology, through a complex of theories with which this was connected, was led on a

new path. For, according to the old idealistic-morphological way
of thinking, the resemblance in embryological development was
evidence only of the common plan, without effect on constancy.
Haeckel, however, proceeds from the principle of evolution and
supposes that similarity points to relationship of descent. This
is plainly expressed when we take notice in which ways, according
to Haeckel, we can obtain knowledge about this descent. He sees
three ways:

   a. *comparative anatomy.* This gives us important data about
relationship, so that Haeckel very readily constructs a genealogical
tree from a "morphological series," while the "primitive form,"
the "archetype," repeatedly is viewed as the real ancestral form.
   b. *embryology.* See above.
   c. *paleontology.* This gives the most definite proofs through
the study of the fossils.

   In Haeckel's *Natürliche Schöpfungsgeschichte* (1868) and
Systematische Phylogenie (1894) one can find many examples
from which it is evident that Haeckel very often uses exclusively
the first two sources of knowledge. We shall mention one such
example.
   When Haeckel discusses the descent of the molluscs, he starts
by saying that the shells of these animals "have very little value
for phylogeny . . . while the real development of the phylum
falls in primordial time, of which no definite fossils have
been saved for us." Fossils are thus entirely absent. That is
why the third source of knowledge mentioned above, paleontology,
fails us. He concludes: "If from thence we wish to construct the
genealogical tree of the molluscs, we are directed providentially to
the record of comparative anatomy and embryology." And with
the aid of that he comes to the following conclusion: "The hypothetical, pre-Cambrian ancestral group of primitive molluscs
(Pre-Mollusca), which died out millions of years ago, we can
place as intermediate forms between the lowest snails, still living,
and the segmented worms. In their ontogeny the interesting
trochophore-larva must have arisen, which today seems to make its
appearance in the embryology of most molluscs."[15]

---

[15] E. Haeckel, *Natürliche Schöpfungsgeschichte,* 12th ed., pp. 423-425,
Berlin 1920.

From this example it appears clearly that Haeckel considered comparative anatomy and embryology sufficient to reach conclusions about descent.

We should point out here that paleontology in principle can give us irrefutable data about the relation between various groups of organisms. It is therefore of decisive importance. In the case of comparative anatomy and of embryology it is different. They can furnish evidence only after evolution has been proved paleontologically. They are in themselves only descriptive sciences. They can discover to which main type an individual or a group of corresponding individuals belong. But they cannot give us phylogenetic data concerning the relations of these types.

It is remarkable, however, how strongly the Haeckelian uncritical phylogenetic interpretations of purely morphological data still dominate present-day anatomy.

To give an example which again has reference to the Mollusca, we cite a recent textbook: "While we do not know exactly what the ancestral molluscs looked like, we can make a very shrewd guess at their structure . . . They had a head with tentacles, a flat creeping foot, a conical visceral hump covered by a mantle which possibly contained numerous calcareous spicules and not a complete shell, and a posterior mantle cavity into which opened the median terminal anus and the common apertures of the kidneys and the gonads, and which also contained the ctenidia," etc.[16] This example could be followed by hundreds of others from recent stardard biological works. They teem with similar Haeckelian reasonings. It is self-evident that what is presented in the partially quoted description of the oldest molluscs is pure typology. This reasoning describes the archetype "mollusc." The Haeckelian component is that this type is called the ancestral form.

When we meet this uncritical tendency in the most recent literature, then the question becomes of great importance: what value should we ascribe to the genealogical trees that we encounter?

We should think of the fact that in the days of Haeckel the investigation of fossils had produced relatively only very little. The

[16]L. A. Borradaille c.s., *The Invertebrata*, 2nd. ed., Cambridge, 1948, pp. 543-544.

paleontological data available were very fragmentary. Most biologists of that time thought that the lacunae could be filled with the above reasonings while they cherished the strong expectation that they would be filled with new fossils that would be found through further investigation. At the same time the conviction was entertained that the transitions from the one group to the other took place very gradually via long rows of "transitional forms." This view is called at times *classic evolutionism.* They felt at liberty to construct long family-trees which progressed from the most simply constructed organisms (*e.g.,* the unicellular plants and animals) to man and other highly organized beings.

Before we review the present state of affairs concerning the question of the origin and descent of organisms, it should be pointed out that at the end of the last century, in a few decennia, virtually all biologists had become adherents of evolutionism. Thus the idealistic morphology and the idea of constancy were eliminated. However, a few exceptions should be mentioned. There remained a few biologists who, sometimes also upon the basis of their Christian worldview, could not accept the general theory of evolution. We shall cite two examples.

The first, born in Switzerland, became the outstanding American zoologist Louis Agassiz (1807-1873). In various books he lodged strong opposition against the views of Darwin and Haeckel. He appears to have been entirely a pupil of Cuvier. Also with him we find the idea of the four irreducible fundamental types. Yet he built upon the ideas of Cuvier in a modern fashion. For example, he discusses Haeckel's biogenetic law. The phenomenon to which this law has reference he views as being based upon the collective structural plan; but, "such comparisons, however, cannot be carried out outside the boundaries of one and the same type."[17]

Agassiz is, accordingly, of the opinion that evolutionistic biology with the study of the embryological stadia, regrettably, lost sight of the boundaries bordering each primary type: "This carelessness in the investigation and in description of facts leads to a too broad generalization which is only partly true; but, to the contrary, is false as soon as it is extended to too wide a field."[18]

---

[17] L. Agassiz, *Der Schöpfungsplan*, 1875, p. 9.
[18] L. Agassiz, *idem*, 1875, p. 11.

He saw clearly that with the first evolutionists many of their scientific hypotheses and theories were directly deduced from their philosophies. He makes the remark that evolutionism is not a theory that is based upon profound research and, starting with the facts, arrives at a synthesis: "no, it is a doctrine which from a notion descends to the facts and searches for facts to support an idea."[19]

Although it is not plain from his works what his position was concerning Christianity, yet in his thinking the motif of creation played an important part: "I believe very definitely that all these relations between the various trends in animal life are manifestations of the Spirit who from beginning to end, self-consciously, pursues a goal. These views are in accord with the workings of our spirit; it is the instinctive recognition of a spiritual power, which reveals itself to us in creation and is akin to our spirit. Upon this basis more than upon any other I consider that the present creation is not the result of the activity of an unconscious organic power, but much more the work of a spiritual self-consciously sustained force."[20]

Although Haeckel had written: "With Louis Agassiz in December 1873 the last opponent of Darwinism descended into the grave, who on the whole deserved scientific respect,"[21] he evidently did not reckon with A. Wigand (1821-1886), professor of botany at Marburg. Wigand published during the years 1874-1877 an extensive work of three volumes, *Darwinism and the Science of Newton and Cuvier.* In this he discusses in detail all the points which in those days were directly and indirectly connected with evolutionism. Also he goes back chiefly to Cuvier in practical biology. Like Agassiz, he saw plainly that the evolutionism of his day made a strong philosophical impact against which he considered it necessary to oppose the Christian creation-motif. A clear quotation from the foreword of the second volume of the work may illustrate this: "I am conscious of the fact, particularly after definite utterances about the first volume, that many readers who agree with my views about Darwinism and materialism, take offense at my reference to the *idea of creation,*

---

[19] L. Agassiz, *De l'espèce et de la classification en zoologie*, Paris, 1869, p. 376.
[20] L. Agassiz, *idem*, 1875, p. 185.
[21] E. Haeckel, *Natürliche Schöpfungsgeschichte, idem*, p. 83.

and are therefore put out about the whole book. However, I should not buy their approbation by stopping halfway and by shying away from the last and the most important question after the same from the other side, and, indeed with correct consistency, had been made the order of the day in connection with the remaining problems. For in fact, we are confronted here in this entire conflict not merely with a scientific question, but with the entire philosophic worldview. And no one can deny that Darwinism, materialism and atheism are in the closest alliance with one another, so that this consequent nihilism, speaking with scorn as well about God as about the laws of science, at least more than all halfway views, may lay claim to being a consistent worldview."[22]

In contrast to adherents of the consistently materialistic evolutionism we can consider Agassiz and Wigand, their predecessors and followers, as representatives of the creationist point of view that wishes to construct a purely scientific biology with the acceptance of all data. The most fundamental background of this view is the conviction that reality owes its existence to divine creation. This way of thinking is in no hurry to make out *how* this creation took place or *what in concreto* was created. Such a proposition is not bound to an evolution-dogma, nor to a dogma of constancy, but it wishes to direct its attention regarding detail problems to the results of research.

3. *Present Knowledge with Reference to Origin of Organisms*

Since the rise of evolutionism the investigation of fossils has been carried on intensively. It is, therefore, of importance for the discussion of the problem concerning the origin of organisms to consider next what has been the result of this investigation. In connection with this we should remark first of all that the oldest fossil remains of animal origin that are known as a certainty, date from the Cambrian Period and are thus 550 million years old according to geological calculation. From times previous to this no animal remnants are known. In many writings this absence of fossils is attributed to two causes. In the first place the conjecture is made that the animals of that era had no skeletal parts so that

---

[22] A. Wigand, *Der Darwinismus und die Naturforschung Newtons und Cuviers*, Vol. II, p. VIII e.v., Braunschweig, 1876.

fossilization could hardly occur. In the second place, it is mentioned that the rock-formations of those times later underwent such tremendous changes that the fossils that were present in them were destroyed.

When we read critically the literature on this, one cannot escape the thought that through these "explanations" the real problem is passed by. One is supported in this by the following remarks.

Gregory, who discusses in detail the question whether these pre-Cambrian animals indeed had skeletons or not, comes to the conclusion: "Although it has been widely assumed that skeleton-bearing forms were derived from older free-swimming creatures without skeletons, I have very gradually come to the conclusion that in many cases the opposite may be true."[23] Furthermore, a number of pre-Cambrian layers are known which have not changed so profoundly and which contain fossil algae. According to Cloud[24] it is probable that if yet other organisms had lived in that age, the fossils of them would have been preserved. Simpson makes the same observation, after which he states the problem that has been mentioned thus: "It is true that most pre-Cambrian rocks have been so altered as to be unsuitable for the clear preservation of fossils. This, however, is not true of all of them, and the exceptions have been so carefully searched that fossils other than algae should have been found if present. There must be some special reason why varied fossils are suddenly present in the Cambrium and not before."[25] The present state of affairs is thus, that from the pre-Cambrium only lower plants, namely algae, are known.[26]

Now, we could be satisfied with this, biologically speaking, if for example, in the Cambrium there appeared first one-celled animals and then later and successively the more highly constructed animals. The problem, however, becomes very great when we see in the Cambrium rather abruptly the appearance of fossil

---

[23] W. K. Gregory, *Evolution Emerging I*, New York, 1951, p. 25.
[24] P. E. Cloud, Jr., "Some Problems and Patterns of Evolution Exemplified by Fossil Invertebrates," *Evolution II*, Chicago, pp. 322-350, 1948.
[25] G. G. Simpson, *The Meaning of Evolution*, 4th ed., New Haven, 1950, p. 18.
[26] Recently I. A. Tyler and E. S. Barghoorn mentioned the presence of bacteria in pre-Cambrian rocks ("Occurrence of structurally preserved plants in the pre-Cambrian rocks of The Canadian Shield," *Science*, 119, 606-608, 1954)

representatives of just about all prominent groups of invertebrate animals: one-celled animals (Protozoa), sponges (Porifera), the sea-nettles (Cnidaria or Coelenterata), segmented worms (Annelida), the joint-footed (Arthropoda), the shellfish or soft animals (Mollusca) and the so-called arm-footed (Brachiopoda).

From these remarkable data it must be concluded that one cannot say anything with certainty or even probability about the mutual interrelationship among these groups in regard to descent. Hence, all that one can read about the evolution of these groups in many publications is not based upon archival parts, but upon Haeckelian speculations concerning the yes-or-no clear correspondence in bodily structure and embryological development among these groups. Thus, where paleontology fails, comparative anatomy and embryology must complete. Carter says about this, although he expresses it weakly: ". . . it should be said at once that any conclusions we can derive from this evidence must necessarily be uncertain and tentative."[27]

Since this method of reasoning, as we saw in the preceding paragraph, is still applied very frequently and because usually it is not realized how completely without value it is for the acquisition of phylogenetic knowledge, let us look at two examples.

The first again has reference to the molluscs. In the *Textbook on Special Zoology,*[28] the best of its kind that has appeared in the Netherlands on this subject, one can read: "There has been no paucity in the various views concerning the problem as to what other invertebrates the Mollusca are related, or from which they probably must be derived. In this connection the Annelida (*segmented worms*) and the Platodes (*flatworms*) share the greatest interest. Most probably the molluscs, in spite of the correspondence in the structure of the body-wall musculature and the larval form, should not be directly derived from the Annelida, since the latter do not possess a digestive gland or a heart, while the segmental organization is absent in the Mollusca. Just as little should the Plathelminthes (flatworms) be viewed as the direct ancestors of the Mollusca. It is true that the structure of

27 G. S. Carter, *A General Zoology of the Invertebrates,* London, 1948, p. 470.
28 J. W. Ihle and H. F. Nierstrasz, et al, *Leerboek der Bijzondere Dierkunde,* Utrecht, 1928, p. 370.

the nervous system and the organization of the larvae in this group have points of correspondence with the Mollusca—although the latter are more specialized—but, in various other respects and in particular because of the absence of the anus and of the blood vessels, the Plathelminthes are differentiated from the Mollusca. It has to be admitted that the three groups, Mollusca, Annelida and Platodes, stand in close relation with one another, so that the opinion is that one common progenitor has been the starting point for all three."

It is striking how with this careful pronouncement no paleontological data are mentioned at all (otherwise the observation would have been made that there are no fossils known at all of the Plathelminthes). It has to be concluded that there has occurred here a mixup of typological thinking ("derived") with phylogenetic concepts ("ancestor," "progenitor").

The second example is one with reference to the descent of the vertebrates. This is one of the few large groups of the animal kingdom which were fossilized for the first time only after the Cambrian Period, when most of the other great groups of animals had already existed for a long time. On the basis of classic evolutionism it is reasonable to expect that fossil remains of the ancestors of the vertebrates would have been detected. However, these links have not been found and for that reason all speculations concerning descent of this group are not based upon records, but upon anatomical structure and embryological development.

Now, in all seriousness, investigators of repute have advanced well-argumented theories which made the vertebrates descend respectively from the sea-nettles (Cnidaria), the comb-jellies (Ctenophora), the Nemertina, the segmented worms (Annelida), the spider-like animals (Arachnoidea), the horseshoe crab (Limulus), the spiny-skinned (Echinodermata) and the lancelet (Amphioxus)[29]. To this long series recently the sea-squirts (Tunicata) have been added.[30] That one, upon the basis of comparative anatomy and embryology, comes to such completely contradictory results proves of how extremely little value the method is. Often

---

[29] See W. K. Gregory, *op. cit.*, p. 89ff.; G. S. Carter, *op. cit.*, p. 469 ff.; A. S. Romer, *Vertebrate Paleontology*, 4th ed., Chicago, 1950, p. 20 ff.
[30] N. J. Berrill, *The Origin of Vetebrates*, Oxford, 1955.

such opinions should be viewed only as typically zoological intellectual games. Thus, it has been discussed at great length whether the Metazoa (multicellular animals) arose from the Protozoa (the unicellular, the animals that are not divided into cells) by a living-together of the products of cell-division or through the appearance of internal partitions.[31] To this Hardy recently added an unexpected third possibility by suggesting that they originated from the Metaphyta (multicellular plants).[32]

As has been remarked earlier, it becomes an entirely different question when evolution is proved upon the basis of fossils. Or, as Schindewolf expresses it: "Over against the *paleontological* evidences they are of lesser importance, since all morphological results of the study of *recent* animals and plants do not furnish historical documents and, therefore they cannot prove at all the historical genealogical development. This can be proved only *from the documents of the past* of which the dates and the succession in time must be known. Thus the exposition of the biogenetic law and of the rudimentary organs is of consequence only if first the phylogenetic development is secured otherwise."[33]

Our conclusion is thus that nothing is known about the origin of the chief groups of organisms, the phyla. However, what is the status of the classes, orders and similar groups into which the phyla can be divided in a natural way?

For various of these subgroups the same thing holds true as for the phyla. Thus, for example, the classes of molluscs and the majority of the classes of the cnidarians appear separated as far back as the Cambrian Period, while nothing can be said with certainty concerning their origin and mutual relations.

Sometimes it is different and there occur regularly classes within the phylum after its first appearance. This is beautifully illustrated by the sequence in which various classes of the subphylum of vertebrates made appearance, namely, in succession

---

[31] G. R. de Beer, "The Evolution of Metazoa," in J. Huxley, *Evolution as a Process*, London, 1954, pp. 24-33.
[32] A. C. Hardy, "On the Origin of Metazoa," Q. J. M. S., *94*, 441-443, 1953.
[33] O. Schindewolf, *Grundfragen der Paläontologie.* Stuttgart, 1950, p. 205ff.

the cyclostomes (Agnatha), fish, amphibians, reptiles, mammals and birds.

An interesting question is, naturally, whether in such instances we can differentiate transitional forms, lines of connection, that lead to new classes. Classic evolutionism expected that the evolution of classes would run smoothly along a series of transitional forms. It was thought that, although not every step of the series was known, many facts indicated that by further investigation of the fossil record the gaps could be filled.

After intensive investigation for the last hundred years, however, many investigators are gloomy as far as these gaps are concerned.

The Swedish botanist Heribert Nilsson has issued a booklet, *The Evolutionary Thought and Modern Biology* (1941), in which he traces what paleobotany at present has to offer as to data about the origin of the types of plants. He starts by going back to what could be called botanical idealistic morphology. Hofmeister (1824-1877), in the middle of the previous century before the rise of evolutionism, constructed a kind of morphological series of the higher plants with reference to their life-cycles and embryology: mosses, ferns, water ferns, cycads, conifers, angiosperms. When later the evolution theory arose, this morphological series was changed into a phylogenetic tree. All the higher plants were supposed to have descended from mosses in the sequence mentioned above. Nilsson remarked correctly that, if paleontology should offer facts for this phylogenetic tree, there would be no objection to this reasoning. However, according to Nilsson, the facts point to something entirely different. The mosses, which one would expect first, appear only at the end of the Mesozoic Era in the Cretaceous Period, while the seed plants (Spermatophyta), which have been placed at the end of the series, arose already in the Paleozoic Era, principally in the Carboniferous Period, in the form of pteridosperms. Since in the Silurian Period no higher plants have made their appearance and in the Devonian Period the pteridosperms and probably also the ferns arose suddenly, the reasoning must be abandoned that the development of the higher plants occurred gradually before the Devonian Period. At the end of the Paleozoic Era the whole flora of pteridosperms

disappeared again as suddenly as it came. At the beginning of
the Mesozoic Period there appeared suddenly new and entirely
differently constructed seed plants, the Bennettitales, which later
on became entirely extinct. And this group of plants was again
entirely different from the present seed plants. Nilsson remarks
in reference to this: "These three groups show three entirely
independent constitutional types, plans of structure, reaction-
complexes, or however one wishes to express it."[34]

The modern seed plants, the Angiosperms, appeared suddenly in
the Lower-Cretaceous Period without the possibility on our part
to record special progenitors. At that time many of the recent
genera and even species made their appearance. The Cretaceous-
flora was even richer in forms than the recent; it was, however,
not more primitive.

From all this Nilsson concludes: "The great earth-floras appear
to arise as demarcated spheres of variation. They show only
succession, no evolution,"[35] and: "There they stand, without any
connecting links, all at once complete and all at once in the greatest
multiformity. Now and then an entirely new type of vegetation
occurs, without our ability to find the prerequisite ancestors. This
succession without evolution, with intermittent periods of a
tabula rasa, is reminiscent of the view of Cuvier about the origin
of the world of organisms."

In connection with this publication on the part of botanists,
the German zoologist O. Kuhn has traced what data paleontology
gives us concerning the relation between the subgroups of the
vertebrates.[36] The first vertebrate animals arose during the
Ordovician Period. They were remarkably formed fish-like
beings which are counted with the class of Agnatha (jawless
ones), of which, as far as we know, the only survivors are the
lampreys and allied creatures. Already these vertebrates occurred
in great variety, so that it is even necessary to differentiate five
irreducible types among these animals that arose fairly well
simultaneously: "according to our present knowledge there are

---

[34] H. Nilsson, *Der Entwicklungsgedanke und die moderne Biologie,* 1941, p. 19.
[35] H. Nilsson, *op. cit.,* p. 21.
[36] O Kuhn, "Typologische Betrachtungweise und Paläontologie," *Acta Biotheoretica, VI,* 55-96, 1942.

many structural plans present within the Agnatha which even theoretically cannot be traced back to one another."[37]

Late in the Devonian Period the sharks made their appearance with two different types, without being connected by transitional forms with the Agnatha mentioned. Equally revolutionary, the bony fishes appeared in three great groups (Crossopterygii, Dipnoi and Actinopterygii). The same holds true for the various types of amphibians and reptiles, the first land animals that arose, and for the birds. According to Kuhn the various groups of mammals also arose separately from one another during the Mesozoic Era, without demonstrable transitional forms.

Just as Nilsson, Kuhn draws a few conclusions from these data which are diametrically opposed to classic evolutionism, which presupposed gradual transitions. Thus he says, for example: "We have no complete phylogenetic trees at all, no trace of them could be found."[38] "We have, therefore, no exact proof for continuous genetic relations . . . . With the question about the origin of the types we have at last reached the boundary of scientific knowledge."[39]

His conclusion is: "Never does one find those forms which could be placed on the ramifications of the phylogenetic tree. No matter how short-lived they were, if they ever lived, some of them should have been found in the overabundance of material. But they have not lived, and the types, from the beginning of their appearance, were separate. That is why we also find only the continuous orthogenetic series, these, however, in great number. That, and nothing else, paleontology teaches us. We should draw the logical conclusions finally and accept the facts the way they are, instead of pursuing preconceived fanciful phylogenetic trees for the love of preconceived notions."[40]

From the publications of Nilsson and Kuhn it is very clear that a new voice is heard in paleontology. The classic evolution theory, which wants to explain all evolutionary phenomena by way of gradualness, has only secondary value according to these investi-

---

[37] O. Kuhn, *op. cit.*, 1942, p. 64.
[38] O. Kuhn, *op. cit.*, 1942, p. 69.
[39] O. Kuhn, *op. cit.*, 1942, p. 84.
[40] O. Kuhn, *op. cit.*, 1942, p. 88.

gators. It alone can explain the further differentiation of the given types which have originated in an unknown way. As the phenomenon of evolution, viewed in the sense of the plasticity of types, it retains its force also for them. Kuhn expresses himself clearly on this point: "The fact of descent remains. Only, descent beyond the typologically circumscribed boundaries is nowhere demonstrable. Therefore, we can indeed speak about a descent within the types, but not about a descent of the types."[41]

We see, therefore, that at present there are again investigators who wish to go back to the idealistic morphology of the beginning of the previous century and that they wish to extend this science only with the aid of the data which paleontology has found in the meanwhile; without wishing to assume in advance that the evolutionary presupposition is the solution to all questions. This is expressed clearly in the application which Kuhn has given of this in his *Lehrbuch der Paläozoologie* (1949), at the beginning of which he remarks: "In our systematic work we abandon first entirely the origination of the differences. We merely establish the existing differences and simularities, and this we bring to expression in the system. The relations of the forms to one another are chiefly of an ideal kind and from them the theory of descent has made true genetic relations, a step which in the past neither Goethe or Agassiz dared to risk."[42]   And: "With that the historical consideration of the organisms, which obtrudes itself readily in paleontology, shall in no sense be abolished as being insignificant. Here only the logical primacy of idealistic morphology is stressed. In how far we are justified to translate the concepts of pre-Darwinian morphology into the language of phylogeny is a problem in itself."[43]   One could imagine that the attention paid to the sudden appearance of the types within the phyla occurred only with a few extremists. That is not the case at all. Everywhere they begin to direct their attention to this phenomenon and many realize that here we have one of the most fundamental problems within the framework of the question concerning origin. We

---

[41] O. Kuhn, *op. cit.*, 1942, p. 94.
[42] O. Kuhn, *Lehrbuch der Paläozoologie*, Stuttgart, 1949, p. 4.
[43] O Kuhn, *op. cit.*, 1949, p. 5.

find this, among others, with Böker,[44] Schindewolf,[45] Gold-schmidt,[46] Rensch,[47] Simpson,[48] and Mayr.[49] It is correct when Davis[50] says: "practically all students of evolution agree in recognizing an element of real or apparent discontinuity in the origin of a major adaptation." This phenomenon does not remain confined to the classes but is also to be stated about the lower categories. Thus Simpson [51] points out, for instance, that paleontological investigation has not been able to establish transitional forms which lead to the 32 orders of mammals, and then he continues: "This regular absence of transitional forms is not confined to mammals, but is an almost universal phenomenon, as long has been noted by paleontologists. It is true of almost all orders of all classes of animals, both vertebrate and invertebrate. *A forteriori,* it is also true of the classes themselves and of the major animal phyla, and it is apparently also true of analogous categories of plants."

In recent times there has been an important trend among investigators who think that the "Lücken," these "gaps," are not to be attributed to the defectiveness of fossil material that is present but that we have to do here with a factuality in the sense in which Schindewolf says that, "gradual transitional forms between the individual types have never lived."[52]

This conviction has had the result that on the one hand the phenomenon of these "gaps," which formerly were usually explained away, have become a problem of the first order in modern evolutionary investigation; but, on the other hand, there is developing a change in the explanation of evolution.

---

[44] H. Böker, "Artumwandlung durch Umkonstruktion," *Acta Biotheoretica, I,* 17-34, 1937.

[45] O. Schindewolf, "Beobachtungen und Gedanken zur Deszendenzlehre," *Acta Biotheoretica, III,* 195-212, 1937.

[46] R. Goldschmidt, *The Material Basis of Evolution,* New Haven, 1940.

[47] B. Rensch, *Neuere Probleme der Abstammungslehre,* Stuttgart, 1947.

[48] G. G. Simpson, *Tempo and Mode in Evolution,* New York, 1947.

[49] E. Mayr, *Systematics and the Origin of Species,* New York, 1942.

[50] D. D. Davis, Comparative Anatomy and the Evolution of Vertebrates," in *Genetics, Paleontology and Evolution,* Princeton, 1949, p. 81.

[51] G. G. Simpson, *op. cit.,* 1947, p. 106 ff.

[52] O. Schindewolf, *op. cit.,* 1937, p. 205.

Classic evolutionism wanted to explain evolution only upon the basis of the uniformitarian principle which has been universally accepted since the days of Lyell (1797-1875). Through his work, *Principles of Geology* (1830-1832), Lyell brought about a revolution in geology of the same nature and of the same extent as Darwin's later reformation in biology. Lyell defended the thesis that we should not explain the changes that have taken place in the earth's crust in the past with the aid of mysterious catastrophes (Cuvier), but with the aid of processes in nature which we can still observe today. Through this so-called uniformitarianism Lyell became the great antagonist of Cuvier. On his trip around the world Darwin tested and approved the geological views of Lyell. It was evident that through this he came to the idea that in a comparable way the changes in the world of organisms in the past must be explained with the aid of actual processes. This idea led to classic evolutionism with its gradualness and thus its transitional forms.

The changes which occur in recent organisms are attributable chiefly to selection, mutation and isolation.

The designated new trend, however, thinks that with the aid of these mechanisms the origin of types of a higher order than, for example, species and genera, and perhaps families, cannot be explained. Processes must have been enacted which biologists have not yet observed in nature. And with that the uniformitarian principle, which teaches us continuity, is rejected. For this *neo-evolutionism* substitutes evolutionary processes which were much more radical in nature, and thus it comes to the evolutionary view of discontinuity. To state it briefly in the language of Schindewolf, one of the foremost neo-evolutionists: "There must be here original discontinuities, natural jumps in development, but not accidental circumstances and gaps in fossil conservation."[53]

That a fundamental change in regard to classic evolution is meant appears from the following quotation of Schindewolf: "Our paleontological record has led us, in contrast to the classic doctrine of descent, to the confirmation that the individual

[53] O. Schindewolf, *Der Zeitfaktor in Geologie und Paläontologie*, Stuttgart, 1950, p. 128.

structural types are not connected smoothly into one long chain of transitional forms with small steps of transformation and that their individual characteristics are not continuously bridged, but that they appear to be separated from one another by great jumps."[54]

As far as this point is concerned, biology finds itself at an impasse, since with the establishment of these "gaps" there is a return, at least theoretically, to the situation of a century ago. Hence Meyer remarks: "If one wishes to hold fast to the theory of descent and does not wish to return to the old doctrine of Linnaeus of an 'infinite Being' as the Creator of all species, then there is in fact nothing left than to search for new possibilities of the real-historical deduction of separated types of species."[55] We shall review a number of these neo-evolutionistic explanations.

Through Böker the theory has been framed of the "transformation of the species through reconstruction" ("Artumwandlung durch Umkonstruktion"). He tries thereby to combine the mutation-selection idea with the Lamarckian view, which explains evolution through an adaptation-activity of the organism. He proceeds from the assumption that there is great internal contrast between the *anatomical character* and the *anatomical construction*. Thus there also exist different changes of species, namely, one which rests upon changes of single characters which are generally indifferent for the life, for the adaptation, of an animal, and one, the "reconstruction" of an anatomical structure, through which the animal at once is fit into a new environment. The first kind of transformation of species is investigated by geneticists, the second kind should be studied by the morphologists. "The geneticists, who inquire experimentally in laboratories and experimental gardens, never investigate anatomical structures! That explains why the geneticists on the one hand and the morphologists on the other hand so often do not understand each other and fight each other fiercely."[56]

The morphologist, through studying the anatomical structures, can

---

[54] O. Schindewolf, *op. cit.*, 1950, p. 200.
[55] A. Meyer, *Ideen und Ideale der biologischen Erkenntnis*, Leipzig, 1934, p. 141.
[56] H. Böker. *op. cit..* 1935, p. 20.

contribute to the understanding of those evolutionary modifications which transcend mutation-selection changes.

Böker makes this plain through an example. In South America there lives a gallinaceous bird, *Opisthocomus cristatus,* and in New Zealand the parrot, *Strigops habrothilus.* Both have a very large crop for the gathering and grinding of food (which consists of woody parts of plants and leathery leaves). They are very much hindered in their ability to fly because the crop lies in front of the chest instead of in front of the throat, as is the case in most other birds.

About the manner in which this aberrant type of bird originated, Böker has constructed the following theory: he takes for granted that the ancestors of these birds, just as their closest relatives, devour chiefly insects and fruits. As the result of a sudden change in climate a new type must have come into existence, thanks to "reconstructions," in which three "anatomical reactions" can be differentiated, which are not founded upon changes of single characters but of anatomical structures.

The first cause of this was that, as a result of climatic changes, these birds had to eat very hard leaves. As a result of that the first anatomical reaction took place, namely, the formation of a large crop. This "reconstruction" had an important influence upon the equilibrium of the body because the weight of the neck, head and crop together became greater than that of the posterior half of the trunk. The center of gravity moved anteriorly, as a result of which these animals had a tendency to fall forwards. This disproportion was the cause of a second anatomical reaction whereby, through the growing out of the tail-feathers, an attempt was made to restore equilibrium, while at the same time, through enlargement of the flight-feathers of the wings, an attempt was made to retain the ability of flight of these birds that had become heavier. These attempts, however, did not succeed, with the result that the crop was shifted backwards in the direction of the center of gravity.

It then began to occupy a place anterior to the sternum. This interfered with the muscles of flight and became the cause of a third anatomical reaction: Reduction of the muscles of flight and, hence, of the ability to fly. Böker observes in this succession of disturbances in the bio-morphological equilibrium and the anatomical reactions a clearly directed process which, in his opinion, cannot be caused by accidental happenings such as mutation and selection. The explanation is to be found only in a "sensible active reaction of the totality of the animal, directed towards the future." The total animal thus adapts himself actively to the changing environment.

One can exercise criticism upon this example of Böker and upon his theory by pointing out that there are no fossils available which would prove that his description of the former structure of these birds is correct, but especially also because the probability is that the changes in climate and in food, which were the ultimate causes, progressed only very slowly. If that is correct, then the anatomical reactions also must have transpired slowly. This means that the factor of gradualness can be introduced. And this includes the possibility that all the phenomena can be explained with the aid of mutation and selection. Therefore, the theory of Böker is not able to explain the presence and the crossing of the "gaps." In addition, this theory lies in the area of species (*"Artbildung"*) and the "gaps" are especially of significance for the origin of higher categories.

A second theory has been proposed by Schindewolf.[57] As an illustration of his theory he makes use of his observations of definite fossil nautiloids (a group of cephalopods). In strata of the earth of different ages, the skeleton of these animals has a very different structure. The oldest ones of a certain series, according to Schindewolf, had a straight skeleton. Then followed those that had at the first part of the skeleton, thus the part that embryologically was built first, a small spiral curve. With the later ones the skeleton is rolled up more and more into a spiral. Upon the basis of this he stated: "The new type-character appears here sport-like and suddenly at the beginning of the shell, thus in the early developmental stages."[58] How dangerous it is to construct such a series upon fossil-material of this kind appears from

---

[57] O. Schindewolf, *op. cit.*, 1937.
[58] O. Schindewolf, *op. cit.*, 1937, p. 197.

the assertion of Flower[59] that Schindewolf's series should be read partly in reverse, namely, that there occurred a despiralization instead of a spiralization. For the rest, this author also is of the opinion that in those cases where spiralization did occur it happened suddenly, like a "saltation."

From this and other observations Schindewolf arrives at the conclusion about his "law of the early ontogenetic origin of types." This law says "that the exhibition of new types, the acquisition of fundamental, that is, of mostly qualitative new, complexes of characters, progresses sport-like in the more or less early stages of ontogenesis."[60]

As we saw, he (Schindewolf) is convinced that the new types appear suddenly in the strata of the earth, often in a very rich variety of species, without the previous presence of transitional forms. Thus Schindewolf, as other investigators, differentiates in a type two phases: (a) "the phase of the explosive early ontogenetic origin of types," which usually takes only a short time, and (b) "the phase of the restful, gradually progressing differentiation" of this new type-complex.

In the following sentences Schindewolf renders his verdict on classic evolutionism: "In the first period the development is discontinuous; sportive and without transition, there originate here fundamentally, that is, qualitatively, new organizations. During the second phase, in contrast, the progress of the phylogenetic development is continuous. It shows here an orthogenetic change of characters of a quantitative kind, documented by numerous transitional forms, upon the basis and in the framework of the organization-texture formed during this first period. Only this second phase corresponds to what till now generally had been considered the essence of phylogenetic development."[61]

As an explanation for the sudden early-ontogenetic formation of types he thinks he should accept: "spontaneous radical changes in the heredity substance which make their appearance from time to time."

It is clear that this explanation of Schindewolf is also very speculative. Paleontologically it cannot be proved and it is very

[59] R. H. Flower, "Saltations in Nautiloid Coiling," *Evolution* 9, 245-260, 1955.
[60] O. Schindewolf, *op. cit.*, 1937, p. 201.
[61] O. Schindewolf, *op. cit.*, 1937, p. 201.

improbable that science will establish an early embryological change of that kind.

A third theory is proposed by Meyer.[62] To begin with, he joins forces with the "reconstruction" idea of Böker; but, then, he adds further that only these "reconstructions" are possible which are given in the "germ plasm," hence, in the storehouse of genetic potentialities. What is not given here cannot be realized. He asks then: "How is it possible, in an evolutionary way to get through somatic reconstructions a real increase of the genetic potencies of the germ cells? Our answer will sound: through holobiosis of different types, also through synthesis of types."[63]

He makes plain by an example what he understands thereby. The well-known lichens do not consist of one kind of organism, but, as appears through microscopic examination, they are symbioses of two entirely different kinds of plants, each of which belongs to a different chief type of the vegetable kingdom, namely, of an alga and of a mold. Together they form an apparently entirely new type, the type lichen. Meyer thinks that in this way, through a strengthening of the symbiosis, ultimately, a real, a new type, can come into existence through absolute fusion (synthesis of types) of the two old types. The advantage is clear: here two types come together, each with its own genetic potentialities.

That through such a synthesis of types in the past the great groups of organisms really originated, is very doubtful. The speculative nature of Meyer's reasoning is strengthened by his supposition that, for example, the organs in the bodies of the higher organisms perhaps originated in this fashion.

From the three theories which have been discussed it is evident that it is difficult for a neo-evolutionistic theory to offer an explanation for the gaps which will make a somewhat acceptable impression.

With emphasis it must be pointed out that over against this neo-evolutionism there are a great number of biologists who continue to defend classic evolutionism. They are of the opinion that

---

[62] A. Meyer. "Beiträge zur Theorie der Evolution der Organismen." *Acta Biotheoretica*, 7, 1-80, 1943.
[63] A. Meyer, *op. cit.*, 1943, p. 54.

it is definitely possible for the uniformitarian continuity-mechan-
isms of micro-evolution (mutation, selection, migration and
geographic isolation) to fill the gaps. The views which these
investigators devote to the evolution problem have an advantage
in comparison with those of neo-evolutionists, especially since
in the area of micro-evolution experimental research is possible,
while the hypotheses of the authors we discussed above "escaped
precise definition which would make them subject to experimental
test or any kind of rigorous proof or disproof."[64]

We shall have to follow carefully, therefore, the research of
the more classically oriented investigators and for the time being
we shall not pass judgment upon their momentarily still hypothetical method of explanation. However, we should keep in view
the limitation of their investigations: "A geneticist can approach
macro-evolutionary phenomena only by inference from the known
micro-evolutionary ones. It is obviously impossible to reproduce
in the laboratory the evolution of, for example, the horse tribe. . ."[65]

However, against their views there are to be adduced two
additional objections. In the first place, with the help of these
mechanisms, as far as the present status is concerned, can be
explained the transformation of definite structural parts and the
eventual loss of subdivisions of the body, but not the origin of
entirely new structures. In the second place, these investigators
usually call in the aid of a change in intensity of the processes in
order to explain the formidable differences which sometimes arise
in a short time with the origin of a new type. However, the
acceptance of these differences in intensity signifies, in fact, the
abandonment of the original uniformitarian principle.

A third objection has been advanced by Voous: "Yet, one asks
himself the question whether the total picture of the evolution of
the living organisms has become more understandable through the
accumulation of the morphological, cytological, physiological,
ecological and ethological differences obtained through the geo-
graphical formation of species. According to my opinion, no.
And even though I attribute much value to the meaning of micro-
evolution, it is not possible for me to presume that the great

---

[64]Th. Dobzhansky, *Genetics and the Origin of Species*, New York, 3rd ed.,
1951, p. 17.
[65] Th. Dobzhansky, *op. cit.*, 1951, p. 17.

systematic groups of today originated exclusively in that fashion. Especially the micro-evolution of marine organisms induces me to scepticism. The present predominating limited possibilities of geographic variation of marine (not brackish water) organisms, especially as the result of their great possibility of distribution in one or another early phase, must be very disadvantageous for an intensive geographic process of species formation. Inexplainable, it seems to me, by way of micro-evolution, is also the tremendous evolvement which marine organisms showed in the oldest geological times, together with the fact that all, or nearly all, great systematic groups originated in the sea, and still have their representatives there."[66]

It would take us too far afield within the space of this book to go deeper into this question. Many biological data and concepts would have to be introduced, but it would not be of significance for our theme as far as the ultimate result would be concerned. It is sufficient that we maintain that micro-evolution, thus that of species, has been proved. But, for the time being, we should consider it problematical whether the mechanisms which caused this could also have been the factors that dominated the genesis of the higher categories.

4. *Creationism and the Question of the Origin of Types*

Just as with the question of the origin of life, we should ask ourselves what our attitude as Christians is concerning the idea of the evolution of types. We commence again by declaring that the data gathered by science naturally must be accepted. If we do not do that then we do violence to the truth and no science is possible. Just as in the previous chapter, we have attempted as much as possible to separate the discovered data from hypotheses and speculations.

We thus obtain the following picture: From the Pre-Cambrian Period only fossils of lower plants are known. From the Cambrian Period we know of the fossils of many groups of invertebrate animals which appeared suddenly. After the Cambrian Period there appear successively several kinds of other main

---

[66] K. H. Voous, "Zoogeographie en evolutie," *Vakbl. v. Biol.*, 30, 155-164, 1950, p. 163.

groups, whereby it is significant that no transitional forms are known.

From these data one must conclude that it has not been proved definitely that there was a gradual evolution out of one another of the higher categories which can be differentiated in the vegetable and animal kingdoms. This has been one of the most surprising discoveries of paleontology, since it is in conflict with the expectations which evolutionism cherished everywhere in the preceding century. In order to obtain a proper picture of the course of events it should be pointed out that with these data a distinction must be made between the phyla as main stems and the categories of lower groups, such as classes. About the origin of phyla, as we saw, no intelligent word can really be said. With the classes the case is different. Although on account of the absence of intermediate forms no convincing proof can be given of the evolution of groups of the systematic order of classes, and although no mechanisms are known definitely through which the eventual transitions have occurred, this does not mean that all arguments are lacking that plead for such an evolution.

The most important argument is the parallelism which we sometimes observe between the successive appearances of new classes and their changed anatomical structure. Or, as Schindewolf says: "The most important proof which paleontology gives is the circumstance that the individual phyla, classes, orders, etc., of organisms make their appearance in such a temporal-historical succession as corresponds with their increasing organization and height of development."[67] (Schindewolf exaggerates somewhat by stating wrongly that this phenomenon also occurs with the phyla.)

When we observe in the strata of the earth that of the sub-phylum of the vertebrate animals there appear at first exclusively the jawless, then the fish and further successively the amphibians, reptiles, mammals and birds, and when we see thereby simultaneously how, ascending in this series, various organ-systems, for instance, the nervous system, circulatory system and renal system, exhibit a clearly directed change, then the conclusion is obvious that there must be a relation among those groups.

---

[67] O. Schindewolf. *Grundfragen der Paläontologie*, 1950, p. 197.

Hence, although absolute proof is lacking, the factual material often gives an important indication of the evolution of classes. The same holds true, in many cases in an even stronger measure, for the genesis of categories of lower order.

The fundamental question for us as Christians, in connection with the genesis of types, is whether we, upon the basis of our faith, are compelled to pay homage to a definitely sharply circumscribed concrete opinion regarding the origin of groups of organisms. Is it necessary for us, in orthodox Protestant circles, to hold fast to the opinion so often current among us, that God has created all these groups out of nothing (special creations)?

Since we derive our faith from and test it with Scripture, we can reduce this question to the problem whether the Bible gives us certainty concerning this. In the previous chapters we have seen that Scripture does not give us scientific data. Nor do we find in Genesis photographs of fossils, tables, graphs or computations. We have also established that if we take the texts literally, "let the earth bring forth," etc., we can sooner read into this, translated into scientific language, a concrete evolution than a creating out of nothing. But we pointed out that even this conclusion does an injustice to the revelation of Scripture. The Bible does not give us scientific data, but reveals to us truths that cannot be discovered through scientific investigation. We have to understand the texts from Genesis concerning the origin of animals and plants in this sense, that there is revealed to us that all organisms came into existence at the command of God ("God said"; "the Word" from John 1) and according to his plan ("after their kind").

These revealed communications should also form part and parcel of the faith and worldview of the biologist. And since in connection with the problem of evolution we have to deal with more than simple facts and laws, these parts of our faith indeed exercise an influence also within the thinking of the biologist about the origin of groups of organisms. Because, then it becomes our conviction that the origin of the phyla is not something capricious and accidental, but that it has been willed, with intent, thus and not otherwise. The same holds for the classes and all the lower categories. And if then we can explain the genesis of definite organisms with the so-called aid of undirected mutations and blind selection which operate by way of so-called laws of chance, the Christian knows that these fit into a directed framework and that beyond them lies a plan. This plan as such cannot be discovered scientifically and God's direction can be experienced only in faith. But this plan and this direction are for the Christian just as real as that which is established in fossils and in genes.

The Christian knows that God caused the organisms to exist at his command, but he does not know *how* and *where* and in which way this happened. These questions lie in the territory of science.

When we apply these principles to the question of the origin of types, we arrive at the following conclusion: We must view this question in the light of the divine plan that has been revealed to us, to form man in the entourage of a living world. The appearance of new types is in that case not exclusively the result of accidental undirected mutations in union with accidentally fortuitously selecting and isolating external circumstances, but all this obeys the command of God.

The investigation has taught us that the transition of one type into another, if it did take place, must have been executed through a complex of extremely complicated processes and which presumably are completely unknown to us. We should be able to picture a type that must change into a new type, for instance, a reptile into a bird, in the imagery of a very complicated safety vault with a great number of combination locks. From such a safety vault the contents can come to the outside only when, by means of a very improbable method, the letters are combined in a very definite way. The ascertaining investigator declares that this combination was established fortuitously. The Christian thinks that a personality, that God, ultimately has made all and has directed it in such a way that the combination had to be realized.

Over against the materialistic-evolutionistic view we place the creationistic idea which includes the possibility that new types originated through concrete causes (possibly mutations, selection, early-ontogenetic type-origin, reconstruction, etc., etc.), but that no absolute chance dominated these processes; that, to the contrary, they all fit as pieces of a mosaic in the plan of God with this world. The plan which, for instance, is so evident in the genesis of the vertebrates (Agnatha, fish, amphibians, reptiles, mammals, man) and the abruptness of the genesis of types, even argues for this creationistic line of thought. They plead for it, but, of course, they naturally do not prove it. The element of creation in our line of thought issues from our faith, in the same way as the purely chance actualism issues from a consistently materialistic faith.

To be very concrete, creationism can take the point of view that in all probability within the phyla an evolutionary process took place. This, however, occurred according to a definite divine plan. For instance, an evolution of mammals from reptiles and of amphibians from fish should not be excluded when we take into consideration the successions which have been established by paleontology. As we noticed, we get the impression that the intermediate forms are missing. Possibly there has been no gradual transformation in the sense of classic evolutionism. Rather, we should think of a complex of now improbable processes happening but once in their combination.

Formerly we once designated God's direction as "abrupt creative intervention."[68] This unfortunate formulation was at times confusing, even though we added that it must be understood in the sense in which we explained it above. Thus writes Van Nieuwenhoven: "His view can be summarized thus, that he wishes to see the origin of all the missing links in the evolutionary chains, hence, the origin of new structural schemes of plant and animal, as separate creations, thus as separate interventions of the creating God. It seems to us that in this way he is in great danger of reducing the influence of God upon evolution to the action of a *deus ex machina*: when one cannot get there with natural means he has to resort to supernatural forces. Without denying the possibility of this, we prefer to view the 'creation by God' more from a metaphysical point of view. Creation, does it not, signifies the total dependence in essence and existence of the entire world upon a creating God. And this should not be conceived of as an initial push, through which the world got its start, after which it was left to itself and developed itself all or not into higher forms, but as a continuous dependence in existence and operation. Therefore, it is difficult for us to agree with the opinion of Lever, which

[68] J. Lever, *Het Creationisme.* Inaug. Vrije Universiteit, 1952, p. 21.

of course, places creation and evolution next to each other as two causes on the same level: when the one cause is not sufficient, the other one fills in what is lacking."[69]

We wish to point out that Van Nieuwenhoven expresses his agreement with the passage (for us unacceptable) of the Encyclical *Humani Generis,* of 1950, of Pope Pius XII. He cites from section 36: "The Catholic faith obliges us to hold that the souls are immediately created by God."[70] In this way he gets into flagrant contradiction with his principally stated former expression about "intervention." It may be presumed that Van Nieuwenhoven will abandon his chief objections after the explication given here which is more detailed than was formerly possible. The difference that was often mentioned between the *that* of creation and of divine guidance and the *how* of the genesis leaves the way open for scientific investigation and causes us to await calmly the results, without preconceived notions. Creation and evolution do not lie on the same level, but evolution is subservient to and is entirely circumscribed by its preceding and determining creation.

What is stated above had particular reference to the evolution of classes. What has been imparted holds also, of course, for the genesis of lower categories.

The question about the origin of the phyla, the highest categories, still remains. About this, as we stated, no scientific data are known at all. One should, reasoning from the orthodox Protestant tradition, be inclined to speak here of the "creation out of nothing." This cannot be contradicted on the basis of investigation.

However, we should leave here two other possibilities, especially in connection with the conclusions we stated in the chapter on the origin of life. We saw that creationism can retain the possibility that the realization of the created entity of life may have taken place by way of improbable yet natural processes. This contains first of all as a possibility that, from the life which came into existence the various phyla first originated in a series in a way (up till now) entirely incomprehensible. Which series that was, one cannot say. The second possibility is that the phyla all

---

[69] L. M. van Nieuwenhoven, S. J., *Biologie,* Roermond, 1954, p. 228 ff.
[70] L. M. van Nieuwenhoven, *op. cit.,* 1954, p. 278.

arose independently. If that idea should be confirmed, it would mean that with most of the phyla we deal with truly irreducible groups, hence, with separate subkingdoms within the creation. This would be in line with the views of Cuvier and of the idealistic morphology.

Although we do not know how this phyla-genesis has taken place, we are sure that it was not dominated by a purely closed immanent system, but that it was purposefully directed and controlled by God.

The creationistic point of view about the origin of the phyla does justice to all the data and leaves the way open for various scientific hypotheses. But it holds fast to the idea that, no matter which data are available and no matter which hypotheses may be correct, the most exalted explanation of this origin lies in the purposeful and determinative primarily creative action of God and the direction of all developmental processes through Him.

CHAPTER FOUR

THE CONCEPT OF SPECIES AND THE PROBLEM OF ORIGIN

1. *Introduction*

Within the framework of the general problem of evolution the question of the origin of species occupies a very important place. There are several reasons for this. In the first place, long before the evolution theory arose heated discussions were carried on about the concept of species, which had a philosophical background and the results of which are still evident today. In the second place, because of the abrogation of the concept of constancy of species in the previous century, for many the way was opened to the complete theory of evolution. Finally, the species question occupies a central position today in the study of evolution, since the changes which can be observed and evoked in living organisms usually have exact reference to the characters of species. Thus, according to uniformitarian classic evolutionism, as we saw in the preceding chapter, in the case of the mechanisms which cause these changes, we have to deal with the authors of total evolution.

In this chapter we shall consider first the history of the concept of species and the content which it is accorded today. Then, as in the preceding chapters, we shall review to what extent a Christian should take a special position in the problematics of species, especially in as far as it has reference to the question of origin.

2. *The History of the Concept of Species*

Already the Greeks (e.g., Aristotle) used the words "eidos" and "genos," which we know as "species" and "genus." These concepts, however, did not yet have specific biological meaning. They were general terms that were used in common parlance to designate a definite group of objects that could be divided into various subdivisions. Thus we can speak of the "genus" furniture and then designate tables as "eidos," or to use a biological example: "genos" aquatic animals, "eidos" fish. These terms thus give us a linguistic expression of the first naive-logical classification upon the basis of the peculiarities of objects observed by the senses.

We thus must emphasize that the concept "species," and also the concept "genus," originally were pre-scientific and not biological concepts. Before there was anything like a scientific biological systematics, the concepts that would form its basis already existed.

The transition of the common parlance to scientific thinking took place during the Middle Ages when these concepts were fitted into the framework of scholastic thinking. In medieval philosophy one of the most important questions was that of the *universalia*. In reference to this the philosophers were divided into realists and nominalists. This separation is of importance for this reason, that in later times these two currents of thought constantly are met again in the interpretation of the concept of species.

Our intellect, in reference to the images of sense-perception, gathers into concepts a certain generality which ostensibly appears in corresponding objects. The universalia problem is the question concerning the relation between these concepts and reality.

The occasion for the statement of the problem was a passage of Porphyrius' (252-301) *Eisagoge,* rendered after the German translation of Radl: "Since these words, 'genus, species,' have a definite meaning for the intellect, the question arises whether that which enters into the definition of the genus, *i.e.*, whether this or that genus beyond the intellect, in nature itself represents a reality, a true entity, differing from every other. Are the species and the genus realities. . .or only conceptions of the intellect. . ?"[1]

The solutions to this problem are to be differentiated into:

1. *realistic* — which[2] can be divided chiefly into the *ultra-realistic*, principally of the 9th and 10th centuries, which presents the general entities as substances that manifest themselves in single objects, so that these thus participate in general realities; and the *moderate-realistic* from the later Middle Ages which holds that general concepts formed by the intellect indeed exist as such only in the intellect but, nevertheless, find a basis in reality.

2. *nominalistic* — the nominalists recognized only one substance, namely, that of empirical objects. Concepts are only constructions of the mind and abstractions. Or, as Diemer formulates it: "The content of consciousness in nominalism has reference to physical reality and no longer to metaphysical forms as with Aristotle and realism."[3]

The opinion of Thomas Aquinas (1225-1274) has been of great importance. He tried to create a connection between the Christian faith and Aristotelian philosophy. Like Aristotle, he differentiated in the separate objects a double element of independence, namely, indefinite matter and definite form, the "morphe." The independence-form defines that which is essential in man, animal and plant. Our knowledge originates through contact between our intellect and the material world; it is a true knowledge of the morphe. Hoogveld says tersely: "The form is the realization of an idea and can be transposed again, so to say, in an image of knowledge,"[4] and "The abstraction is thus a deeper

---

[1] E. Radl, *op. cit.*, I, p. 263.

[2] F. Sassen, *Geschiedenis der patristische en middeleeuwse wijsbegeerte*, 1942, p. 93 ff.

[3] J. H. Diemer, *Over biotypen van Anopheles maculipennis Meigen, in het bijzonder in Westelijk Nederland*, 1935, p. 188.

[4] J. H. E. Hoogveld, *Inleiding tot leven en leer van S. Thomas van Aquino, Nymegen*, 1939, p. 88.

grasping of the form, of the idea realized in the objects."⁵ This
idea, known to us through abstraction, is not different in each
individual, but can be realized by many simultaneously. We thus
get a conception of the universal.

If it had remained that way, the moderate realistic opinion of
Thomas would not have been of such great importance for later
pre-Darwinian biology. With Thomas, however, we also find an
answer to the question about the origin of the ideas of which
forms are a realization. According to him and also, for example,
with Albertus Magnus (1206-1280), they existed in the mind of
God before creation. In this synthesis of Greek philosophy and
Christian faith the universalia have a threefold formal existence:

ante rem, from eternity in the mind of God,
in re, as the corresponding similarity in individuals and
post rem, as abstraction in human thought.

This scholastic way of explaining the origin of species has
exercised a very great influence upon the development of biological systematics; but, above that, it has aided strongly the
aversion on the part of Christians against the possibility of an
evolution of species. The present-day species afterwards were
strongly tied, as constant structural entities, to the individual acts
of divine creation.

Nominalism, particularly in the form of the empirical direction
dominated by the Englishman Locke (1632-1704), at least initially,
has exercised little influence upon biological-systematic thinking.
According to nominalism, knowledge is possible only through the
inductive method, by means of the sense-perceptions of the
phenomena. Science, however, may not attribute metaphysical
importance to this.

The preceding views were directed only at the philosophical
world of ideas of the Middle Ages. We now have to turn to
biology. There was in those times definitely a pre-occupation with
the direct study of plants and animals. With that, however, in
general, they had in mind another purpose than that of modern
biology. The systematics was oriented, namely, in imitation of

⁵ J. H. E. Hoogveld, *op. cit.,* 1939, p. 93.

Dioscorides (1st century A.D.), towards pharmacology. It was a subdivision of medical science.

The influence of Dioscorides was twofold. In the first place, with the aid of his flora of Greece, an attempt was made to determine the plants from all over Europe. It took a long time, in fact to Brunfels (1488-1534), before people became conscious of the fact that the flora of Dioscorides had only local value. Not entirely unjustly, therefore, Linnaeus called Brunfels "the Father of Botany." But, in the second place, for centuries after Dioscorides there continued division of plants upon the basis of utility: curative power, poisonous character, etc. In the 16th century there came a change, but it did not immediately result in a separate, conscious biological-systematic description of plants.

The botanist Clusius (1526-1609) in his *Historia Stirpium Hispanae* of 1576, broke with the utility principle and even used a binomial nomenclature; but in his *Historia Fungorum* of 1598 and in his *Rariorum Plantarum Historia* of 1601, he again divided the plants according to their noxiousness, edibility and the like.[6] Also Rumphius (1628-1702), who thus lived much later, was still strongly attached to the principle of utility.[7]

Gesner, Aldrovandi and other writers of herbals often still based their system upon the classification of Aristotle, and did not formulate a solidly defined concept of biological species and genera. Caesalpinus (1519-1603) took a different course by building his Aristotelian system upon the basis of the really vital functions, such as growth, nutrition, respiration. He thus divided the plants according to their organs of nutrition into wood, plants and herbs. The concepts of species and genus he still used in the undefined Aristotelian sense. That his purpose to obtain a natural system, based upon the really natural characters was realized only much later, is evident from what has been told about Clusius and Rumphius.

In the 17th century it finally became necessary, because of the enormous quantity of plants and animals that were newly discovered, to search for a vastly circumscribed unity for the system.

---

[6] J. Theunisz, *Carolus Clusius*, Amsterdam, 1939, pp. 67, 136, 137.
[7] G. Ballintijn, *Rumphius, Utrecht*, 1944, 38, ff.

To this it should be added, as related in the previous chapter, that gradually through the influence of physics and chemistry eyes were opened to the fact that the wealth of forms was limited and was ruled by law and order.

As there appeared an increasing consciousness of this latter need, the question became urgent in which direction this unity should be sought. The ultimate choice has been of great significance for the background of the problem of evolution.

Theoretically there was a possibility of two directions:

1. In the first place, one could search for empirical, biological criteria which would make it possible to determine the genetic-organic connection among individuals of various groups by assembling for instance, those groups of plants and animals which copulate and produce fertile offspring in confrontation with other biotic features.

2. One could also devise a biological concept of species which, it is true, could coincide entirely practically with the preceding but which would be placed in the framework of the traditional form-metaphysics and whereby the metaphysical universalia-problem and the "ideas of creation" would be put in the foreground. The biological aspect of the concept of species, in this case, would be superseded by the second plan.

It was the English investigator John Ray (1628-1705) who made the choice for biology and, to be sure, in the second direction. This was the result of his scientific training, or, as Diemer remarks, "On the one hand through his extensive knowledge of nature and, on the other hand, through his philosophical and theological training, he was the designated systematician to investigate thoroughly the theoretical basis of the species-concept."[8]

In the thinking of Ray we find a mixture of nominalism and realism. This is because he first with his theoretical knowledge joins the nominalistic point of view of Locke and thus comes to the conclusion that every systematizing and every combination of individuals must be artificial. We cannot know the essence of the objects round us since we are dependent upon our sense organs. He accepts, however, that the repeated observation of a certain combination of characters may find its cause in the essential

---

[8] H. Diemer, op. cit., p. 191.

similarity in the nature of the individuals concerned. In addition, in answer to the question concerning the metaphysical cause of the natural species-entities, we find in Ray the same scholastic reply as that of Albertus Magnus and Thomas Aquinas, and because of that his opinion has been of such great importance for the struggle with the problem of evolution. He says: "The individuals of what we call a species appear to have been made after one and the same idea in the mind of God, just as machines which all are manufactured in a factory according to one idea. It is probable that all species originated, not by bringing into commotion matter of one kind or another, from which issued various forms, but because God created them all simultaneously in the beginning."[9]

This is exactly the same idea of the origin of fixed species which we still find today among many orthodox Protestants. What precedes indicated how this idea originated through a linkage of the scholastic-philosophic way of thinking with the early assumption of a certain separation of groups among the living organisms. This is an unstable basis for the idea of the constancy of species.

According to Ray, the species are created as constant, natural units, really distinguished from one another. There is thus also a direct genetic connection between the present-day species and those from the beginning of creation. The constancy of species is for him self-evident and follows logically from his philosophic-theological point of view. The problem of descent does not appear in his works; he evidently did not see the importance of it.[10]

As far as the biological definition of species is concerned, Ray came to the conclusion, as expressed by Uhlmann, of the "through hereditary transmission specifically constant form" ("durch Vererbung spezifisch konstante Form"),[11] with as criteria the morphological conformity, the *form-principle,* and the potentiality of forming a fertile progeny, the *hybridization-principle.* This

---

[9] J. Valckenier Suringar, *De geschiedenis der verwantschapsidee in het plantenrijk,* Meded. v.d. Landbouwhogeschool te Wageningen 36 (1), p. 21, 1932.

[10] *Cf., e.g.,* his essay about "The Number of Plants" in E. Lankester, *Memorials of John Ray,* London, 1844, pp. 207-214.

[11] E. Uhlmann. *op. cit.,* 1923, p. 16.

does not deny the fact that Ray also had an open eye for the small changes which specimens of a species can undergo. However, he views these as changes of the accidentalia, not of the essentialia. At any rate, he did not see them as symptoms of evolutionary processes: "The *'transmutatio specierum'* meant for him evidently not yet a way to the answer to the question about the origin of species."[12]

In order to follow further the development of the concept of species we now have to discuss Linnaeus (1707-1778). Linnaeus, in connection with his practical botanical work, does not think about the origin of the *concept* of species in line with the theory of knowledge as was the case with Ray. He viewed the species in the first place as real entities which, as such, occur in nature as groups of individuals united through blood-relationship. Linnaeus, accordingly, viewed the species as natural realities.

Although Linnaeus was more of a practical bent of mind, the thought of the ideas of creation (among others, through the influence of Leibnizian trends, as we saw in the preceding chapter), so generally present in his time, exercised influence upon his views. He accepted again that the order among the species was instituted by God and he considered it the purpose of systematics to explore this order. Systematics should strive after a "natural system." He is conscious of the fact that his system is "artificial" to a large extent, but he cannot do anything about it as yet. He must create order in the great quantity of plants and animals, otherwise biology cannot operate.

Famous is his expression that there exist at present just as many species as God created in the beginning: *"Species tot sunt quot diversas formas ab initio produxit Infinitum Ens"* (*Gen. Plant.*, 1737).

There has been much discussion about this expression. All kinds of meanings have been attributed to it.[13] It is more important for our subject to point out that many investigators have attempted to charge to the account of Christendom the dogma of

---

[12] E. Uhlman, *op. cit.*, 1923, p. 17.
[13] See J. Lever and H. Dooyeweerd. "Rondom het biologisch soortbegrip I," *Philosophia Reformata*, 13, 1948, p. 30 ff.

the constancy of species which certainly is to be found in Linnaeus and which has retarded the development of science.

We find this, for instance, in Lam. He has explored the formulation of this expression in the successive works of Linnaeus. From this it appears that Linnaeus afterwards realized that the species are not as constant as he thought initially, as a result of which he attached the constancy more to the genera. Thus, according to Lam, Linnaeus was the first one to doubt the constancy of species and for that reason he became the precursor of evolutionism. Lam opines that this dogma of the constancy of species is a typically Christian line of thought which has retarded the development of evolutionistic views of which the pattern already can be found in the Greeks. He says: "In the glorious age of science of ancient Greece, and perhaps earlier, there was sufficient insight into the multiplicity of forms in organic nature to warrant the supposition that it was possible to make an arrangement of steps of development of successive value. It is likely that this liberal philosophy one day would have resulted in an objective explanation of this material, if a serious obstacle had not presented itself: the dogma of Christianity with its literal interpretation of the story of creation and its anthropocentric worldview. Of course, a literal interpretation of Genesis implies the immutability of all that has been created; hence of the species, and where change is excluded, evolution is out of the question."[14] Hence Christendom, long before Linnaeus, adhered to the dogma of the constancy of species and in that way hindered Greek thinking in developing itself. Only with Linnaeus does doubt begin and the way is opened for evolution.

However, when we examine history, it appears that this proposition is not correct. The Greeks indeed often had the impression that nature is not constant. This expresses itself clearly in the complex of ideas to explain the phenomenon of spontaneous generation that had been observed by them. However, the peculiar fact remains, as we have pointed out expressively in preceding chapters, that the scholars of the Middle Ages, hence Christendom, held fast exactly to this Greek thought *in biology,* if we may express it thus. The same holds true for the change in form that

---

[14] H. J. Lam, *Evolutie,* Leiden, 1946, p. 27 ff.

was observed. We noticed that Albertus Magnus (see page 60) imagined that wheat could change into rye, and the like. Even though in philosophy the realistic opinion generally was held of the constancy of the universalia, this had not yet been transposed to the constancy of biological species. The term species had not yet been defined and confirmed as a biological concept. Therefore, Clark has stated entirely correctly: ". . . it is clear that the doctrine of the fixity of species was no part of the intellectual climate of the Middle Ages, and far less was it an article of Christian faith."[15]

Where did this idea originate? After the discovery of strange countries there was introduced into Western Europe a great variety of unknown plants and animals. One thus got the idea that the variation in nature was unlimited. At the same time there was no conception as yet for definite law and order in structure and hence, there was a belief in the existence of the most grotesque monsters.

In the 16th and 17th centuries, however, experimental science began to develop and it was observed that inorganic nature exhibited constant structures and fixed laws. This had its repercussion in biology: it was observed that the spontaneous generation idea was incorrect and that the organisms did not transform into one another. As Clark says, "It was a result of these considerations and observations that, for the first time in history, the doctrine of the fixity of species was propounded."[16] The basis for this dogma thus became observational science. This received a religious significance only when Ray tied the observed fixity of species to the realistic-scholastic view of "ideas of creation."

To this should be added that the theoretical background of the "ideas" of Linnaeus' thinking is strongly reminiscent of and probably also, via Leibniz, influenced by one of the most important thinkers of Greece, namely Plato (to which, e.g., Meyer[17] refers) whose ideas have been Christianized by the church fathers and the medieval philosophers.

In summary, against the belief that the dogma of fixity of

[15] R. E. D. Clark, *op cit.*, 1948, p. 34.
[16] R. E. D. Clark, *op. cit.*, 1948, p. 39.
[17] A. Meyer, *Krisenepochen und Wendepunkte des biologischen Denkens,* Jena 1934, p. 121 ff.

species is of a typical Christian character and that it retarded the development of Greek thought, it can be argued that it had its origin in a fusion of observed law and order with the Christianized Greek philosophy.

Besides, it should be observed, as we stated in the preceding chapter, that we should view Linnaeus more as a precursor of the idealistic morphology that rested upon the idea of fixity, than of evolutionism. This becomes clearer still when we see what value Linnaeus attached to the changes he observed, and on account of which he afterwards altered the formulation of his pronouncement somewhat. Linnaeus noticed after his later cross-breeding experiments that there were indeed possible changes and variations. This variation, however, according to him, does not affect the essential characters which alone may be taken up in the diagnosis of the species, but the accidental characters that can vary under the influence of the environment. Cuénot reflects the views of Linnaeus as follows: "Variety is a plant mutating because of accident, climate, soil, heat, wind; that is to say, that the varieties are non-hereditary modifications of little importance; the botanist is not concerned about fleeting varieties (*Philosophia botanica*, 1751, no. 100)"[18] And Hugo de Vries says when he speaks about the variations in plants: "Even when the same variation arises anew in a number of specimens and for years in succession, its chances of being discovered are only very small. Besides, our methods in studying wild plants have become gradually very definite. The influence of Linnaeus here is still felt very strongly. We are very sensitive to the differences between systematic species, and every new species immediately draws our attention. We are less sensitive, however, to minor differences; yes, in a certain measure we have become indifferent, and most likely they are missed by us."[19]

Next we should consider what the influence has been of advancing evolutionism upon the development of the concept of species. Here also Lamarck must be counted a pioneer. In his *Philosophie zoologique* of 1809 he devotes a special chapter to the subject,

[18]L. Cuénot, *l'Espèce*, Paris. 1936, p. 21.
[19]H. de Vries, *Experimentele evolutie*, p. 187.

"Concerning the species among the living organisms and the idea which we have to attach to this word."

Lamarck begins by remarking that it is not easy to circumscribe what we understand by species and also not easy to investigate whether species indeed are fixed and thus as old as nature, or whether it is possible that they change extremely slowly under the influence of external circumstances. He agrees with the description that we should understand by species every collection of corresponding individuals that have been produced by their kind. But he lodges a serious objection against the addition, current in his day, that the individuals that belong to a species never change their specific characters and that thus the species is fixed.

Lamarck remarks that this addition owes its origin to the times in which the organisms had not been studied sufficiently. Investigation in the days of Lamarck was entirely in conflict with this view, so that the biologists had the greatest difficulty to determine the organisms. Definite specimens are viewed as varieties in one country and in another as species. The phenomenon that definite organism-populations resemble one another so strongly and, that as long as they have been known they have remained so precisely similar that one considered himself justified to view them as immutable, he considered the cause for the view that species are fixed. This immutability, however, for him exists only apparently, namely, as long as the outward circumstances remain constant. Lamarck is right to a certain extent in his attempt to explain the view concerning the fixity of species, but he could have added to this (as, *e.g.*, has been remarked by Hugo de Vries) that the variations, which also occurred, were viewed as unimportant and that, besides, an important cause lay in the scholastic metaphysics of the ideas of creation.

Lamarck also noticed that there was something wrong with the religious interpretation of all this. He says concerning the idea that all the species have been created separately by the Creator: "Doubtless, nothing exists but by the will of the Sublime Author of all things. But can we set rules for Him in the execution of His will, or fix the manner He has used? Could not His infinite power have created an *order of things* which gave existence successively to all that we see as well as to all that exists but that we do not know?

"Assuredly, whatever His will may have been, the immensity of His power is always the same, and in whatever manner that supreme will may have asserted itself, nothing can diminish its grandeur.

"Thus respecting the decrees of that infinite wisdom I confine myself within the limits of a mere observer of nature. So, if I succeed in unraveling anything of the route nature has followed in making its products, I shall say without fear of error that it is thanks to its Author that it has that faculty and that power."[20]

Up to that time it had been sufficient to describe the sharply divided species, but, as the collections of plants and animals became larger, the boundaries faded out and there remained only sub-ordinate particularities to maintain the distinctions. "I do not wish to say by that, that the existing animals form one simple series, regularly graded throughout, but I do say that they form a branching series, irregularly graded and having no discontinuity in its parts, or, at least, not always having had it, for it is alleged that there are found some, owing to some species having been lost."[21]

Then Lamarck traces what might have been the cause of this. He establishes that there are many facts which point out that according as the individuals which belong to a species change as to place, climate and mode of life, they undergo the influence of these changes in the sense that through these there is a gradual modification of their form, functions and mode of life. As a result, in time their character changes entirely and thus they have formed a new species which differs clearly from the originating species. This reasoning contains the idea of active "adaptation" and of "inheritance of acquired characters," which indeed has been designated as *Lamarckianism*.

What value this has and against what background the preceding was viewed by Lamarck becomes evident when he thereupon poses six propositions which, in a concise form, typify classic evolutionism:

[20]J. B. Lamarck, *op. cit.*, pp. 38-39.
[21]J. B. Lamarck, *op. cit.*, pp. 40-41.

1. That all organized bodies of our earth are true products of nature, that she has wrought successively throughout long periods of time;

2. That in her procedure, nature began and still begins every day by fashioning the simplest organized bodies, and that only these she fashions directly, that is to say, the rudiments of organization designated by the term *spontaneous generations;*

3. That the rudiments of animals and of plants fashioned in suitable places and conditions, supplied with the properties of commencing life and of organic movement, necessarily have developed the organs, and that in the course of time, they are differentiated, just like their parts;

4. That the property of augmentation of every part of the organized body, inherent in the earliest manifestations of life, gave rise to different kinds of multiplication and reproduction of individuals, and that thus the acquired increase of the composition of the organization and of the shape and the variety of characters has been preserved;

5. That with the help of time, of the conditions that were necessarily favorable, of the changes successively undergone by every part of the earth's surface, and, in one word, of the power of new conditions and of new habits to modify the organs of living bodies, all those which now exist have been fashioned imperceptibly, such as we now see them;

6. That, finally, after such an order of events, the living bodies having undergone every greater or smaller change in their organization and their characters, that what we call *species* among them were imperceptibly and successively fashioned, having only a relative constancy and being not as old as nature.[22]

From these fundamental theses of Lamarck, it appears clearly that his criticism of the old concept of species resulted from his view regarding the general problem of origin. In this setting a constancy of species is simply impossible. His deviation from the old concept of species does not proceed primarily from his biological experience, but from his modified worldview. For, when we examine all these six theses closely, no cogent argument could be adduced for any of them at the beginning of the preceding

---

[22] J. B. Lamarck, *op. cit.*, pp. 45-46.

century. Lamarck evidently was not merely "a simple observer of nature." The synthesis in the Middle Ages between religious belief and philosophy led to the view of the ideas of creation. In the case of Lamarck, as we saw, this resulted in deism, which views God as the First Cause.[23]

Although Darwin in the choice of the title for his work with which he made the evolution theory acceptable, *On the Origin of Species by Means of Natural Selection,* indicates that the species problem is of central importance for the evolutionary view, he has contributed little to the theoretical reflection upon it. This work has been accomplished by one of his followers, namely, Haeckel. The concept of species which he proposed is no concept of species in the old sense of the word, but much more an entirely new construction. He considered the phyla as the entities of the system, taken in the sense of the series of descent of the classic species depending upon blood-relationship.

But also from another point of view there is in the post-Darwinian period of species-investigation an entirely modified manner of thinking: in the pre-Darwinian period constancy generally was referred to an ideal substance. On account of that the thoughts of the biologist were not centered upon the question concerning the all-or-non-presence of material bearers of characters. There was no search after "fixed attributes of every species" (festehende Attribute für jede Spezies), as Leibniz called them. He considered it necessary that we should possess the "penetrating sight of higher Spirits" in order to know the attributes referred to. Every species was viewed as an entity, which had to differ also in its entirety from all other species, because of their realization by God, at the beginning, after different ideas.

Darwin was the first one who in his life's task directed the gathering of biological material for the idea of evolution, to call attention to the fact that distinctions of species must be based upon the characters of species, and characters of species upon material carriers. He proposed very provisionally and very carefully his theory of pangenesis[24] to explain the genetic phenomena of varia-

---

[23] See quotation on p. 70.
[24] In his work *Variation of Animals and Plants under Domestication,* 1868.

tion and of the inheritability of acquired characters. He suggested that the characters are linked to material germs, the pangenes, which are present and are formed in every part of the body. From thence they are transported to the germ cells which transmit them to the progeny.

In the latter half of the previous century there have been many more investigators who thought in a similar direction. Thus Möbius[25] saw a similarity between the experiments of the growers of plants and animals and of the chemists. Just as the latter, the former work with elements: "with definitely present factors, upon the characters of which they are dependent, when they wish to breed new products."

Hugo de Vries succeeded in giving definite content to these genetic trains of thought and at the same time to establish a clear contact between the question of species and of evolution. We see this in the following expression: "When we observe the characters of the species in the light of the doctrine of descent, then it appears soon that they are composed of individual factors, more or less independent from one another. Almost every one of these latter one finds among many species, and their changing grouping and combination with the unusual factors postulate the extraordinary multiplicity of the world of organisms."[26]

This meant a fundamental break with the old concept of species with its constancy and sharp demarcation. It is, as de Vries expresses it: "Under the many advantages of outstanding importance which the doctrine of descent has bestowed upon the investigation of organic nature, the abrogation of the old concept of species occupies a prominent place."[27]

The attention paid to the articulateness of the genetic phenomena was, on the one hand, a gain for evolutionism and this idea was accepted eagerly; on the other hand, a difficulty arose. Because we should realize that for the first evolutionists, who had parted with the dogma of the fixity of species, the organisms and the species appeared more or less plastic. For these investigators of plants and animals there was no principal constancy of structure.

[25] K. Möbius. *Die Bildung. Geltung und Bezeichnung der Artbegriffe und ihr Verhältnis zur Abstammungslehre*, Jena, 1886, p. 32.

[26] H. de Vries, *Intracellulare Pangenesis*, 1889, in *Opera*, 5, p. 8.

[27] H. de Vries, *op. cit.*, 1889, p. 8.

This changed, and with this we approach the core of the matter, when Mendel (1822-1884)) and his followers, through ingenious experiments, discovered the laws of genetic phenomena and thus the structural constancy of genetic material. And when in addition it was stated that the hereditary characters are bound to material bearers, the genes in the chromosomes, and when Boveri in 1903 succeeded in establishing a synthesis between the knowledge of the hereditary phenomena and that of the mitosis-phenomena, and when cytogenetics thus came into existence, and Morgan even could localize the place of the genes in the chromosomes, the problem of the evolution of species obtained an entirely different relief. It was seen that, although the structure of an organism during its lifetime could often adapt itself to the environment, this "pheno-type" had absolutely no repercussion upon the "genotype." From various experiments it appeared that the idea of "inheritance of acquired characters," which with Lamarck as with Darwin was found to be an essential point of their evolution-theory, did not correspond with the facts. And through this the organisms, in the eyes of the investigators, lost their plasticity which they possessed according to the old evolutionists.

An important influence upon the further development of biological thought was exercised by Weismann (1834-1914)[28] who placed emphasis upon the fact that within the organism one can make a distinction between the "soma," which reaches its development through the interchange with the environment, and the sex-cells, the "germ-plasm" which undergoes no influence from the soma, and thus also not from the environment. Through the generations runs the uninfluenced thread of the "germ-plasm," the "germ-path" (Keimbahn) which is constant and continuous. This idea of the "continuity of the germ-plasm" signified a strong obstacle for the old evolutionism, because neither the adaptation of Lamarck, nor the natural selection of Darwin, could explain sufficiently the evolution of species. The selecting environment, naturally, according to this idea, is hindered in its evolutionistic power through the limited number of constant genes. It can select only the favorable, but then evolution is finished.

It was Hugo de Vries who, as it were, rescued evolutionism

---

[28] A. Weismann, *Die Continuität des Keimplasmas,* Jena, 1892.

through the discovery of mutation, which has been verified every-where. He and his followers found that the "germ-path" is not absolutely constant, but that now and then, through causes that have generally not been clarified, in an, as far as we know, undirected way, small changes occur in the genes. This means that there is principally a break in the constancy of the genetic potency. This, naturally, has its repercussion upon the soma, through which the mutation obtains a selection significance. According to this view the environment has not to deal any more with a definite number of constant genes, since possibilities are added. Through this idea of mutation the Darwinian theory of selection became modernized.

After having thus demonstrated succinctly that the modern idea of heredity (founded in material factors) and the evolution theory became important for the question of concept of species, we should observe next how this has led to the greatest possible confusion.

Because, if there was formerly unanimity of opinion about the concept of species, after the rise of evolutionism the opinions became divided. This was because some investigators wished to put emphasis more upon the genetic aspect, others upon other aspects of the organisms and of organic life. But this was also because there was no longer unanimity on the question whether species and/or the remaining systematic categories had a real existence or were only the figments of the imagination. Moreover, it was a question whether the essential distinguishing features of the categories had a constant character or whether all the characters of the individuals were variable.

One would be inclined to think that we find in this simply a continuation of the old antithesis between realism and nominalism. One would create confusion, however, if he designated the schools of thought which after Darwin held fast to the natural reality and eventually to the constancy of the categories, simply "realism" and the other, in contrast, "nominalism." For the contrast realism-nominalism was rooted in the fundamental motif of Greek thought, that of form and matter. It concerned the question whether there existed immutable ideal "forms of being" which transcend the flowing current of emergence and decay (the "matter principle" or "hyle"). As we saw, scholasticism adapted this Greek form-principle to the biblical creation-motif and thus constructed out of the Greek forms of being the "ideas of creation."

However, after the Middle Ages in philosophy, and after the rise of the evolutionary idea in biology, there came into existence an entirely different approach to nature. The new natural science strove for the domination of nature and tried to discover the causal relations. The Greek-scholastic attitude of thought over against nature was substituted by one of domination which operated by way of an analysis and a synthesis of the phenomena. The position, on account of this, became more and more nominalistic in nature. Through the departure of the creation-motif and the change-over from "description" to "analysis" the thought about the "eternal ideas of creation" was gradually eliminated from scientific thinking.

When, therefore, after Darwin, in biological circles there is a discussion anew about the reality and about the eventual constancy of species in respect to other categories, then there usually is a consideration of a reality and a constancy that can be defined empirically and that has no metaphysical significance.

When thus after Darwin, in reference to the view concerning the categories, we differentiate two main currents, of which the first one recognizes the reality and, in a certain sense, the constancy, while the second denies these, then the antithesis which reveals itself here coincides only partly with the controversy of the Middle Ages between realism and nominalism.

Thus one can detect in the first main current a strong anti-metaphysical tendency, which, when the categories are viewed as real and in a definite sense as constant, does not mean at all to acknowledge the reality of "universalia" in the sense of "general forms of being," but has in view only the material bearers of the characters of species. In genetically oriented biology one can meet with such trends of thought.

Next to that, one also finds opinions that as yet move in the direction of the ideas, whether in the sense of "ideas of creation" or in a more modern sense. One finds these, as can be understood, especially with typologically oriented investigators.

Over against this first main current, which eventually could be designated as "pseudo-realistic," there is a second which definitely does not view the species and the higher categories as realities and takes the nominalist position all along the line. Also within this current two directions can be distinguished. First of all there is the phylogenetic direction which denies the real existence of the categories in the sense of constant units with typical characters and recognizes only as units of the natural "system" the evolving and thus changing "phyla." Further, there is a direction which views the categories only as products of the intellect, which imposes its order upon nature. One could call this the *critical* direction, in imitation of Kant.

The preceding division into four groups is quite broad and not by any means can every author be fitted into this scheme. That is a natural objection to all schematization in science, but it is necessary to make it possible for us to see the background more clearly. It should be remarked also that in the preceding there is talk not only of "species" but also of the higher categories. This is connected with the fact that there are investigators who accept variability for a more or less large number of the lower categories (species, genera, and the like), but who want to view, for instance, the classes and phyla as constant. Such investigators, naturally, may be designated as realistic or pseudo-realistic.

Next, we shall review a few examples of the four groups. The first main current is directed towards the real units and searches for them. As we saw, we first of all find this in the genetically oriented systematics.

Thus with Alexis Jordan we find the idea of "petites espèces" (small species) which Lotsy[29] relates as follows: ". . . in fact there are genetic differences within the Linnaean species, and as according to Linnaeus himself, the inheritability of the characters is the criterion of the species, Jordan concluded, entirely logically, that there are within the Linnaean species different types which, in so far as they transmit their characters unchanged to their descendants, should be viewed as species, so that in reference

---

[29] Lotsy, *Evolution im Lichte der Bastardierung betrachtet*, 1926, p. 372.

to these, the Linnaean species represents a genus." Hence Jordan thought that within the Linnaean species he could distinguish definite small genetic groups which could be considered as units of the system. Lotsy remarks here correctly that between these "petites espèces," these "jordanonts," there is a possibility of hybridization phenomena, which is in conflict with the old definition of the concept of species, so that Jordan was mistaken. That Jordan had a tendency to orient himself toward the constancy of species, Lotsy thinks should be blamed on the firm belief of Jordan "in the absolute truth of every word of Holy Writ." Thus Lotsy puts on par the scholastic-metaphysical line of thought with the communication in Genesis. We shall return to a discussion of this confusion at the end of the chapter.

Lam[30] mentions the attempt of the Danish investigator Winge, who in 1917 tried to unravel the natural units in a cytogenetic way. He thought he had found a fundamental character in the haploid number of chromosomes (the number that is present in the germ cells). Thus, a few genera are known of which the species each have a number of chromosomes that is a multiple of the so-called basic number. Thus, for instance, the haploid number of chromosomes of species of roses is respectively 14, 21, 28, 35, 42, and 56 (basic number 7). Cuenot[31] mentions, *e.g.*, species of chrysanthemums with 27, 36, 45, 72, and 90 chromosomes (basic number 9).

According to the majority of the systematists (for instance Lam), the number of chromosomes is a character which is not better than any other. It remains, nevertheless, an interesting phenomenon that within large groups of plants and animals, species as well as higher systematic categories, there is a constancy of the number of chromosomes. Thus all lilies have 24, all orchids have 20 and nearly all gymnosperms have 24 chromosomes. Thus we see that various more genetically oriented investigators have a preference for the search after a constant real basis for their systematics.

The second group, which lets the element of constancy play a role in its thinking, we find in typology. This is, as it were, a

[30] H. J. Lam, in *Het leven ontsluierd*, Utrecht, 1943, p. 295, ff.
[31] L. Cuénot, *op. cit.*, 1936, pp. 52-57.

supplement of genetics, because, for the time being, it will not advance much further than the study of the characters of species and genera. The higher systematic groups we can regulate momentarily only with the aid of typology. It is correct as Naef says: "Type concepts often have been the basis for the establishment of 'systematic categories'."[32]

In this small compass we cannot discuss the entire concept-apparatus of modern typology, but we confine ourselves here to the main question: Is the type a reality? The realistic and the pseudo-realistic currents consider this to be the case. They view the types as substances, as ideas, whether in a scholastic or in a modern sense. Representatives of this group are, for example, Radl, Driesch and especially Lubosch. Diemer remarks concerning the latter: "The type of a distinct species or of a genus is with Lubosch a super-individual unit, a synthesis of the individual differences. The types are ideas which embody themselves in the individual variability of organisms."[33]

The second main current denies the existence of real units. We meet this idea first of all in phylogeny. Pursued consistently this results in an "abrogation of the old concept of species" (Hugo de Vries), as we saw. Phylogeny, which is mostly based upon the evolution theory, cannot do otherwise than abrogate the discontinuity of the old concept of species. The scientific concept of species is born out of realism and always has been, from the nature of the case, a concept of something constant. Naef says clearly: "The doctrine of descent results in its essence in an *abrogation of the concept of species in its most general sense*. When the living organisms which today are present as separate species have common ancestors, they as a matter of fact constitute one single species."[34] As far as evolutionism is concerned there is no constancy: The whole world of organisms, from the first origin of life till today, is one current of continually varying forms.

It is remarkable, let it be recalled incidentally, that there has been no want of attempts to bend this as yet phylogenetic view towards realism, yes, even to unite the Linnaean view of constancy with phylogeny. Thus Wasmann decides to alter the famous sen-

[32]A. Naef, *Idealistische Morphologie und Phylogenetik*, Jena, 1919, p. 19.
[33] J. H. Diemer, *op. cit.*, 1935, p. 207.
[34] A. Naef, *op. cit.*, 1919, pp. 44, 45.

tence of Linnaeus, which we have discussed, as follows: "How should this sentence sound in view of the evolution theory? According to it the systematic species of today do not represent the forms that were created originally, but are the result of a development, which combines the species of the present and the past into *natural series of forms,* whose members are genealogically related, while every one of these can be traced back to an original ancestral form as its point of origin. When we view each one of these as separate with other not related series of forms or phyla as *a natural species,* then we can even today agree with the sentence of Linnaeus . . .Every one of these *natural* species has differentiated itself in the course of the development of the phylum into a more or less greater number of *systematic* species."[35]

That these phylogenetic "species"are no species in the old sense of Ray and Linnaeus is evident when we think about the form- and the hybridization principle. The scholastic-realistic background of Wasmann is difficult to combine with the spirit of evolutionism.

Finally, we must mention the critical nominalistic group. This is a distinct current in *typology*. According to this, typology does not meet with reality. The types are only teleological syntheses of our intellectual ability to judge the natural phenomena. In other words, the old concept of species is no real concept. This idea we find with A. Meyer, for instance, about which we shall say something more soon.

Finally, summarizing what has been imparted about the directions and currents, we come to the conclusion that at the end of the last and the beginning of the present century, in the place of the old scholastic-realistic concept of species, a great number of new concepts arose through the rise of evolutionism. Partly they represent a development of the old concept of species, but largely, however, they contain new instances and logically may not even be called concepts of species.

---

[35] E. Wasmann, quoted after L. Plate, *Ultramontane Weltanschauung und moderne Lebenskunde, Orthodoxie und Monismus,* Jena, 1907, p. 60. Cf. E. Wasmann, *Die moderne Biologie und die moderne Entwicklungstheorie,* Freiburg, 1904, p. 197 ff.

It is interesting that this modification of views had only a relatively insignificant influence upon the definition of species on the part of the systematists. One can even say that with them the old concept of species of Ray has been retained, with the retention of the form- and hybridizaton-principle, but with the loss of the scholastic-realistic background.

Thus Remane[36] has defined the species as "natural continuous propagation-communities; with separate dissemination, the possibility of the restoration of a reproductive union under natural conditions, decides about that which pertains to species." This concept of unity clearly contains the hybridization-principle; however, viewed historically, it is incomplete because there is lacking a reference to the morphological standard.

In that respect the definition of Döderlein and Plate as transmitted by Boschma[37] is complete: "To a species all specimens belong which possess the characters in the description; whereby the condition must be fulfilled that the animals did not live under appreciably different circumstances—further, all specimens that deviate from this, and yet are so intimately united with them through intermediate forms that without arbitrariness they cannot be separated sharply; finally, all forms of which it can be shown that they are united with the first-named genetically and produce a fertile progeny."

Also the concept "syngameon," proposed by Lotsy and Danser,[38] may be called a real species.

That also during recent years the definition of Ray is retained appears from the following description of Mayr: "Species are natural units characterized by their reproductive isolation from other such units. The species of the taxonomists, in so far as based on morphological criteria, are merely inferences from the species in nature. Whenever there is doubt as to the specific rank of a natural population the analysis of the morphological criteria will have to be supplemented by a study of ecological differences and the completeness of reproductive isolation."[39] We shall return to

[36] Cited after J. H. Diemer, *op. cit.*, 1933, p. 151.
[37] Quoted after H. Boschma, *Het soortbegrip*, Leiden, 1931, p. 6.
[38] Cf. B. H. Danser, *Hand. v.h. 4de Ned. Ind. Natuurwet, Congres*, 1926, p. 347.
[39] E. Mayr, "The Bearing of New Systematics on Genetical Problems: the Nature of Species," *Advances in Genetics*, 2, p. 235, 1948.

discuss more in detail the theoretical importance of basing one's concept of species upon a form-principle and a principle of function, as was the case with Ray and associates.

3. The Modern Phase

The theoretical confusion, about some aspects of which we made mention above, became so great about 1920 that a number of investigators made an attempt to regain the balance. In the first place, in a number of publications Naef[40] has set forth the essential difference between the typology which investigates the purely morphological relationship in the manner of the idealistic morphology, and the phylogeny which investigates the "historical" phylogenetic relationship. About the difference in approach between these two sciences and their value for the problem of origin we wrote in the previous chapter.

Next, Meyer[41] has undertaken something similar for systematics in a very astute manner. He points out that we should not attempt to unite various movements that are at odds with one another. Rather, there must be differentiated a number of systematic concepts of unity each of which must play an important role in a distinct branch of morphology. He thus accepts critically the confusion and he thinks that sound progress can be made only by referring each one of the ideals back to its own area. Meyer considers that there are four such concepts of unity that are reasonable: namely, the so-called *taxon,* which has a purely descriptive-systematic meaning and thus can be used in systematics; next, the *phylon,* the genealogical unity, which is necessary for phylogeny; and, finally, two genetic entities: the *"reine Linie"* (the pure line), as designed by Johanssen and the so-called *isogenon* of Lehmann. Hence, pure systematics, phylogeny and genetics could thus continue to operate independently, each with the aid of its own unity.

Such a splitting-up certainly is not ideal, because in that way the unity in biological systematic thinking would be in danger of

---

[40] A. Naef, *Die individuelle Entwicklung organischer Formen als Urkunde ihrer Stammesgeschichte,* Jena, 1917; further op cit., 1919.

[41] A. Meyer, *Logik der Morphologie,* Berlin, 1926; esp. the chapter "Logik der Systematik," pp. 104-170. See for resume, J. Lever en H. Dooyeweerd, "Rondom het biologisch soortbegrip," II, *Philosophia Reformata,* 14. pp. 25-42, 1949.

being lost, as also the unity of conception concerning the essence of the living organic structures.

This danger has increased rather than decreased within the last decennia. What plays, in the first place, an important role in this is that the struggle between the ideal of constancy and that of evolution, although with a different design and with other motives, is not settled by any means. Formerly constancy was based upon scholastic-religious presuppositions and the antithesis was clearly one between the Christian faith and materialistic evolutionism. At present the antithesis has penetrated deeply into science. If, for instance, there was with Kleinschmidt[42] a clearly evident aversion to general evolution as the result of his Christian faith, Heribert Nilsson shows very clearly that he wishes to put himself at a distance from the Christian presuppostions when he says at the end of his publication already cited: "This means that we accept neither a divine creation out of nothing, because we do not know of a synthesis out of nothing, nor a Darwinian creation out of one cell. . . "[43] Even though most investigators do not take such an extreme point of view, many agree that an even somewhat acceptable explanation of the gaps has not yet been provided. A second cause, which, next to the preceding one, increases the confusion is that not only pure systematics, taxonomy, phylogeny and genetics have constructed concepts of unity, but that also various other kinds of branches of biology have proposed suggestions in that direction. Thus, for example, biogeography (for instance the concepts of syngameon, comparium, convivium and commiscuum of Danser),[44] although these usually agree with the real concept of species of Ray, cytology,[45] embryology,[46] ethology (the

---

[42] O. Kleinschmidt, *Die Formenkreislehre und das Weltwerden des Lebens*, 1926.

[43] H. Nilsson, *op. cit.*, 1941, p. 21.

[44] B. H. Danser, *op. cit.*, 1926. *Cf.* for the question of zoogeography and the concept of species also K. H. Voous, "Het soortbegrip in de zoogeographie," *Biol. Jaarb. "Dodonaea,"* 16, 157-167, 1949 and *Hand. v.h. 31e Ned. Nat. en Geneesk. Congres,* pp. 115-116, 1949.

[45] M. J. D. White, *Animal Cytology and Evolution*, 1945.

[46] G. R. de Beer, Embryology and Taxonomy, in J. Huxley, c.s. *The New Systematics,* 1940.

study of animal behavior)[47]animal psychology,[48] biochemistry[49] and also biosociology.[50]

This recent abundance of concepts of unity is no longer stabilized in the manner Meyer (1926) did by attributing to them limited value. In systematics a new movement has begun which strives for an ultimate synthesis. In pursuance of Hubbs[51] this movement is called the "new systematics." Through a book of a similar name under the editorship of Huxley[52] this endeavor has gained much influence. The result of this has been that many wish to make systematics again one of the most important and even the central biological science which in its systematic endeavors has to take account of all the biological subsidiary sciences.

It is clear that this systematics is only just beginning. What animal has been sufficiently investigated cytologically, anatomically, genetically, endocrinologically, ethologically, geographically, paleontologically and the like, so that one can give a distinct picture of the characteristics that typify it?

Here we have a field for research so extensive that it cannot yet be surveyed in its entirety by any means. This new systematics of necessity will make use of the museum with its fixed and dried paltry remains, and in the laboratory and in the field it will study the organisms in their reactions, relationships and behavior.

This new and grandiose perspective for the oldest (biological) science[53] presents, of course, new problems. Because when all the biological subsidiary sciences come with systematic material, then the systematist must pronounce over them a judgment of value. Which prevails, a comparative-anatomical, a physiological or an ethological datum?

It is evident that behind this problem lies the crucial question concerning the composition of the various aspects of the biotic structures. A mechanist will reduce everything to the physical-

---

[47] N. Tinbergen, *Bibliotheca Biotheoretica*, I, pp. 39-98, 1942.
[48] J. A. Bierens de Haan, *Die tierischen Instinkte und ihre Umbau durch Erfahrung*, 1940, p. 37.
[49] H. Munro Fox, *Chemical Taxonomy, Nature*, 157, p. 511, 1946.
[50] One should think about the biosociological communities.
[51] C. L. Hubbs, *Amer. Naturalist*, 68, pp. 115-128, 1934.
[52] J. Huxley, *et. al., The New Systematics*, 1940.
[53] Genesis 2, verses 19 and 20.

chemical. A vitalist and a holist think about something else again. And thus it appears that it can be predicted in advance that the new systematics again, as all other important phases in the history of biological systematics (the scholastic phase, the transitional phase and the mechanistic-evolutionistic phase), will be strongly influenced by the worldview to which the individual investigator pays homage.

Through Diemer,[54] before the new systematics as such was propagated, a new way was pointed out which, as it were, combines or overbridges mechanism, vitalism and holism. In order to understand better the significance of this it is first of all necessary to deal briefly with the three movements in biology that have been mentioned.

Mechanism signifies that all biological phenomena ultimately can be reduced to purely materially physical and chemical processes. Hence, there is no question about a specifically organic forming or regulating principle; nor of, for example, a psychic or social factor. The various so-called modal aspects of reality, which every human being, as it were, experiences (the physical, biotic, etc.), are only *apparently* irreducible. If investigation progresses far enough, it will appear that all these aspects can be traced back to physical magnitudes whereby all instances of law and order can be rendered in mathematical formulae.

Neo-vitalism arose in modern science especially as a reaction to mechanism. The physico-chemical structures and functions of a living being, according to the old vitalism, are dominated by a vital-force (*vis vitalis*). However, when it was found that organic matter can be prepared synthetically, and that all kinds of processes, such as metabolism and growth, are regulated by chemical materials, so-called enzymes, the old vitalism disappeared practically entirely from science. Driesch[55] with his neo-vitalism has attempted to regain modern biology for vitalism. He accepted completely the closed mechanistic law and order of the material-biological processes, but yet he thinks that an immaterial, specifically-biotic factor, the so-called "entelechy," regulates the processes and thus determines the typical structure of each organism.

---

[54] J. H. Diemer, *op. cit.*, 1933.
[55] H. Driesch, *Philosophie des Organischen*, 2 Volumes, Leipzig, 1909.

Neo-vitalism thus displays some correspondence with the metaphysical thinking of the Middle Ages in which the formative entelechy stood dualistically over against passive matter. Driesch, however, continued to deny the metaphysical character of his theory.

Holism assumes a typical organic law and order. Structure as well as function are in constant balance in a living organism. This coordination is a typically biotic one. The factor of order, however, is not an entelechy outside of matter; no, it *is* the relation in time of structure and function. Holism assumes, however, a fading away of the modal boundaries between the physical, biotic and psychical aspects. According to Adolf Meyer, the most important holist of today, all biological phenomena definitely can be translated mathematically. Most holists have as ultimate ideal a biological mathematics. But, and this constitutes a crucial point, the physical mathematics, according to Meyer, is nothing else but a simplification of the biological, and this eventually of the psychical. When one eliminates from a biological equation the typically biotic factors, a physical law will remain (see footnote p. 53).

Diemer thinks that the elements of truth in mechanism, vitalism and holism can be designated as follows:

a. mechanism discovered the functional law-and-order of physico-chemical processes in the living organism;

b. neo-vitalism discovered the law of the organic structure-principle which directs the functional events in the organism;

c. holism discovered the structural-totality of the living organism, which also comprises its physico-chemical aspect. Besides, it discovered the specific functional-mathematical law which lies at the foundation of life.

Diemer, further, associates himself with a vision of reality which is developed by Vollenhoven and Dooyeweerd under the name "Philosophy of the Cosmonomic Idea."[56] This includes these elements of truth in greater compass and comprises all of reality, and in that way presents a synthesis which in its greater delineations is very acceptable.

---

[56] H. Dooyeweerd, *De wijsbegeerte der wetsidee*, 3 volumes, Amsterdam, 1935-36; American Ed., *A New Critique of Theoretical Thought*, Presb. & Ref'd. Publ. Co., Philadelphia, 1952-55.

By way of introduction it should be pointed out that several authors have stated the opinion that there are various aspects to be differentiated in the objects occurring in reality. We shall mention here only one author. In his exposition of his holistic theories, Adolf Meyer starts from some of the views of the French philosopher Emile Boutroux, who thought, about 1900, that reality is differentiated into nine irreducible, "contingent" areas, namely, those which are being studied respectively by logic, arithmetic, geometry, mechanics, physics, chemistry, biology, psychology and sociology.

According to Adolf Meyer, through the advance of research, most of the sharp boundaries between these areas have vanished and at present they exist only between physico-chemistry, biology, psychology and sociology. How Meyer further thinks that with the aid of holism he can bridge also these contingencies, does not matter here.[57]

From this example it appears that in modern biology the attention is directed to a greater number of typical entities than in the days when only mechanism and vitalism dominated biological thinking.

The "Philosophy of the Cosmonomic Idea" to which we have referred, is based exactly upon the idea that the creation displays a number of such "modal aspects" or "spheres of law." Usually the following entities are differentiated: the arithmetical, geometrical, physical, biotic, psychical, logical, historical, linguistic, social, economical, aesthetical, juridical, ethical and pistic.

A thing functions in all these spheres of law. It is plain that a thing does not function in all spheres of law in a corresponding fashion. The physical sphere of law is one, for instance, for a stone, in which it has a subject-function. In the higher spheres of law the stone can be object only of other subjects. The stone itself cannot feel, but it can be felt by an animal or man. It thus has an object-function in the psychical sphere of law. We shall occupy ourselves first briefly with the different subject-functions of living beings, specifically of plants and animals, whereby we keep in mind biological systematics.

---

[57] See, e.g., A. Meyer, 1934, *op. cit.*; *Krisenepochen und Wendepunkte des biologischen Denkens*, Jena, 1935; *Hauptgedanken des Holismus*, *Acta Biotheoretica*, 5, pp. 85-116, 1939.

In every living being there may be distinguished numerable, arithmetical, and measurable, geometric entities. These, however, are always bound to the physico-chemical substrata because they are never realized in themselves. The physico-chemical part of the body, however, does not constitute as such a living structure. A dead plant, which still retains the form of the originally live plant, perishes rather speedily when the physico-chemical substrate is left to itself independently, undirected and ungathered by the biotic entity, which manifests itself through metabolism, growth, respiration and so many other phenomena.

Here the necessity is evident to consider further the cooperation among the entities within the structure of plant and animal. As far as reality is concerned, the various entities can be distinguished, but reality consists only of totality-structures.

Holism means something similar; also according to this view we should regard plants and animals as totalities. However, holism does not leave the constructural entities where they are, but, dissolves them in the highest entity. This we saw already when we discussed Adolf Meyer's idea of the origin of life. "The Philosophy of the Cosmonomic Idea" permits the entities to retain their value and for that reason it can remain closer to the findings of science. Within the total-structures of plant and animal, however, one entity has a guiding function which directs all other entities to itself. The biotic function in the plant induces, as it were, all lower functions upon itself. The psychic function does the same thing in the higher animals.

To clarify this we give the following example:

When an animal under specific circumstances has to perform much work, for example in birds during migration or the building of a nest, the laying of eggs, and the brooding behavior, then the total animal reacts according to fixed psychical laws of behavior which can be investigated by separate sciences, animal psychology and ethology.

During this behavior not only is the psychic aspect of the bird active, but all other aspects cooperate. In the first place, by way of the nervous system there is an influence upon the entire body, but also with the aid of hormones the entire organism is directed to the typical behavior. Specific centers of the brain influence the pituitary gland, which by way of specifically biotic laws secretes various hormones which stimulate to definite functions respectively the thyroid glands, the adrenals, the sex organs, eventually the crop and other tissues and organs of the bird. All these harmoniously and at their proper time assume their place in the total behavior of the animal. But, not only are purely biotic laws set in motion in this way, also the entire physico-chemical part of the bird, fitting into its total behavior, begins to unfold itself.

To limit ourselves here to the thyroid gland, as a result of the increased secretion of the thyrotropic hormone by the hypophysis, there occurs an increase in the excretion and, further, also an added production of the thyroid hormones. These processes run their course entirely according to purely biochemical laws. From the blood, iodides are trapped from which iodine is produced by means of oxidation. This iodine in turn reacts with specific groups of amino acids, (particularly tyrosine) which are present in specific globulo-proteins. Thus, by way of a number of steps, there are formed, among others, triiodothyronine and thyroxin.[58] These substances are released to the blood as thyroid hormones which elsewhere accelerate the metabolic processes of the body-cells.

The formation of these thyroid hormones is a purely chemical process which can also be performed outside the body in a test tube. Hence there is no need in the body of a *"vis vitalis"* or "entelechy." The absolute independence of the physico-chemical processes should be recognized. Only their fitness, their intertwining into the total-structure of the animal and their direction by the psychical and the biotic aspect is typical of their termination within the living structures. But not only is the animal characterized by the typically orderly psychical, biotic and physico-chemical entities of their structures, also geometrically and arithmetically everything operates according to fixed laws.

The resting thyroid gland of the bird, which accordingly is only slightly activated by the pituitary hormone, consists of spherical vesicles the wall of which is formed out of one layer of cells, yielding a purely stereometric structure. When the thyroid is

---

[58] See J. Lever, "De biosynthese van het schildklierhormoon," *Vakblad voor Biologen*, 34, pp. 24-31, 1954.

activated, the cells begin to lengthen in the direction of the lumen of the sphere and the wall thickens. This coincides harmoniously with the production of hormone. In the lumina the thyroid hormone is stored and partly formed. During the increase in the thickness of the wall the cells take the hormone from the lumina and transfer it from the vesicles to the surrounding blood vessels. This increase in the thickness of the wall occurs entirely according to law, depending upon the quantity of thyrotropic hormone secreted by the hypophysis. When just a little more of the thyrotropic hormone is secreted, the walls become somewhat thicker; when less hormone is secreted, the walls again become thinner. When much pituitary hormone is secreted for a long period of time, then it appears that the wall can increase only to a limited thickness. When still more hormone is secreted by the pituitary gland then the wall reacts in an entirely different manner. The maximally increased cells then begin to divide. They divide then, not in an irregular fashion, the one into two, the other into five; no, there occurs here a division into two which is inescapable. It has been demonstrated that the whole phenomenon of the activation of the thyroid spherules, hence the thickening of the wall and the subsequent cell division, as also the total stereometric structure of the vesicles, can be reduced to a number of mathematical formulae.[59]

It thus appears that all entities of a living animal—arithmetical, geometrical, physico-chemical, biotic and psychical—contribute to the total-structure and its changes, without any deprivation of the peculiar laws of each of the entities. Biomathematics can operate with purely mathematical concepts. Also biophysics and biochemistry can imitate outside the living animal, one by one, the individual reactions.

All entities are directed, however, upon the psychical aspects in the higher animal because they must contribute subordinately to the realization of the behavior that is typical for each animal.

It is interesting to trace how we, from that point of view, can study and practice biosystematics. It is clear that a systematics that is based upon dried plants and stuffed animals must be very inadequate. Also other entities will have to be studied. A biological

---

[59] J. Lever, *Onderzoekingen betreffende de schildklierstructuur.* Utrecht, 1950.

system constructed in line with Dooyeweerd and Diemer, therefore, will be a new systematics. Before we enter upon this, we should consider more closely the structure of a living organism.

The arithmetical and the geometrical entities reveal themselves only in the physico-chemical substratum of life. This forms a so-called "individuality-structure."

In the case of the plant there is added to this the typical-biotic individuality-structure, which reveals itself in such processes as, respiration, growth, reproduction and the like, while the highest animals possess in addition to these two the typical-psychical individuality-structure, based upon the central nervous system in combination with the sense organs and muscles, the "behavior-apparatus" or the "sensorium." Thus, these three individuality-structures of the animal, the physico-chemical, the biotic or organic-vegetative and the behavior-apparatus in the animal are interwoven within the "body." Next to this the animal is also interwoven with the environment, through which it itself is influenced from genotype to phenotype, but by means of which, on the other hand, it also forms its "Umwelt."[60]

It is clear that biosystematics always has to base itself upon morphology, since all further entities of the animal are founded upon its matter-space realization in the physico-chemical entity.

On the other hand, systematics will have to direct itself to the species-characters in the biotic phenomena, but especially also to the behavior, since the animal reveals itself in this most typically. It would mean a great loss for systematics if it passed by the psychic entity which the animal possesses and which can be studied only from its behavior.

We shall enumerate a number of examples from which the value of behavior for systematics will be clearly evident.

Lorenz[61] has pointed out how the group of Columbidae, the pigeons, it is true, form an accurately circumscribed group, but

---

[60] For an extensive discussion of the theory of structure used here, see H. Dooyeweerd, "Het substantiebegrip in de moderne natuurphilosophie en de theorie v.h. enkaptisch structuurgeheel," *Philosophia Reformata*, 15, 66-139, 1950. Also, J. J. Duyvene de Wit, *Gezichtspunten voor een integratieve biologische wetenschapsbeschouwing, Inaug. rede*, Amsterdam, 1950.
[61] K. Lorenz, *Folia Biotheoretica*, 2, p. 20, 1937.

that not one morphological characteristic can be named that is typical for the pigeons and thus does not occur with other birds. However, there is a characteristic of behavior in which the pigeons differ from other birds. The latter, namely, drink by scooping water, or through special movements of the tongue; pigeons drink by pump-like actions.

Another example we find recorded by van Oordt.[62] Both species of terns, *Sterna hirundo* and *Sterna paradisea,* differ very little morphologically. However, upon the basis of their brooding-behavior they can be differentiated very well. *Sterna hirundo* starts to brood at once after the laying of the first egg; *Sterna paradisea* only after all eggs have been laid.

Let us also give an example of entirely different animals. A specific genus of slugs, *Limax,* occurs in a great number of different colors, on account of which each systematist divided them differently. Further, the slugs of this genus, morphologically, are practically the same. However, after investigation of the behavior, it became evident that this genus had to be split into six species, since there could be differentiated six different very typical behaviors of mating, which made it impossible that an animal that belonged to one species could mate with one of the other species.

Finally, let us think of the fact that it is usually much easier to distinguish the small songbirds upon the basis of their song than upon the basis of their structure, color and other material properties.

From these few examples it seems evident that the study of the highest individuality-structure can produce very valuable material for the systematist. The most beautiful example we shall meet in the following chapter when we shall discuss the criteria for what a human being is.

In both criteria of Ray it appears that the form-principle is at once acceptable, since the animal is founded morphologically. The principle of hybridization is more complicated, since it is, on the one hand founded upon the correspondence of morphological structures; as, the structure of the chromosomes and the form of the sex organs; and, on the other hand, upon functional-structures,

---

[62] G. J. v. Oordt, *Beitr. z. Fortpflanzungsbiologie der Vögel,* 10, p. 5, 1934.

as, for example, the time of sexual maturity. When two animals are alike in every respect, but the one matures sexually only in April and the other in July, then no fertilization can take place in nature.

But, in the third place, the hybridization-principle has reference to the structure of sexual behavior; choice of biotope, eventual behavior in the building of a nest, brooding, feeding and mating.

With the choice of this criterium, Ray, followed by most systematists after him, made a master stroke.

We should realize, however, that it is not an exhaustive criterium. The form-principle is directed to the entire body form of the animal. It will imply all that which is formed in the animal, macroscopically and microscopically. The hybridization-principle covers only a fraction of the biotic structure and also only a fraction of the behavior-structure, namely, those fractions which have reference to reproduction. It is a practical, very good determination-criterium rather than a criterium that comprises both structures at which it is directed.

In addition to the three structures which can be differentiated in the animal itself, the systematist, through ecologic research, will also have to take up in his views the reciprocal interplay of the organism and the environment. Only then he will have described the organism in all its facets that are accessible to scientific research.

From the foregoing fragmentary review of the history of the concept of species it may have appeared how systematics constantly has moved from the one leading principle to the other.

After the scholastic period, which sought for substances in the species and which derived a constancy-ideal from the supposed ideas of creation, there was a brief time during which the synthesis-ideal of substances and mathematical derivation (Leibniz) exercised influence upon systematics. This, however, was only a transitional period towards the one in which the consistency of the evolution ideal altered biology entirely; as a result of this also the old species disappeared. And we are living in a period in which the modern ideal of the "new systematics" is in vogue with the open question which natural-philosophical line of thought ultimately will pronounce a judgment of value upon the entities of the living organisms. A reflection concerning the structural frame of the organisms is therefore a primary requirement. Only when this has been thought through fundamentally, will the "new systematics" be able to present a synthesis which transcends the attempts that have been made in this direction in the past. Mechanism, vitalism and holism show one-sided views through which they wish to reduce the valuable entities to those of another kind, or they introduce metaphysics and with that unattainable essential factors. Only a vision of reality which recognizes each of the entities and each of the individuality-structures as specifically laid down in the creation, and, therefore, as irreducible realities, and which also has an open eye for their mutual intermingling, shall be able to attain a synthesis in correspondence with the real structure of the organisms. It is evident, however, that this is a harmony for the distant future.

4. *Creationism and the Question about the Origin of Species*

At the end of this chapter we still have to answer the question which position the Christian should occupy in regard to the problem of the origin of species. For every biologist this is a fairly unimportant question, because evidently an answer to this has been given by science. Yet, in orthodox Protestant circles we often still meet with the idea of the "fixity of species." It happens repeatedly that when one declares that he is convinced of the fact that the species are not constant, that he is considered to be unsound. This is sufficient reason to discuss this point more fully.

This idea goes back to the days of Linnaeus, when biological species were defined for the first time. Thence people began to interpret such passages of Genesis 1 as, "after their kind," ("fruit trees bearing fruit after their kind," "herbs, yielding seed after their kind," "winged birds after their kind," "beasts of the earth after their kind," etc.), as if it meant "after their species," as also the South-African translation of Scripture still has it. In addition, it was thought that the texts in Genesis pointed to the constancy of these species.

This reasoning contained two errors.

a. In the first place, to cling to the idea that "kind" means the same as species in the biological sense signifies that one attributes to the writer of Scripture, who lived thousands of years ago, a concept that was defined only about 1650, and of which the real contents, as we saw in connection with the discussion of the "new systematics," is not even known today. One views thus in this reasoning Genesis as a scientific book which imparts to us, among other things, systematic concepts. As we noted already in the first chapter, this is an oversimplification which discredits Scripture.

b. The second error has had worse results. This was that, in pursuance of Ray, the biological species were brought into relation with the realistic solution of the universalia-problem. We have seen how scholastic philosophy adapted the "form-ideas" to Christian thinking by making out of them "ideas of creation." After defining the term species biologically, this adaptation was transferred to it gratuitously. This means that when one loses sight of the fact that the core of the idea of constancy is of Greek-pagan origin, one gets the feeling of being un-Christian and of doing violence to Scripture, when one does not view the biological species as constant. That is one of the reasons why Darwin explained that when he came to the conclusion that the species are not fixed, he had the sensation "like confessing a murder."

The harmful result of these errors revealed itself only when evolutionism arose. Upon the basis of the aforesaid it was not realized that there should be made a differentiation between evolutionary data, scientific evolution hypotheses and theories, and philosophical evolutionism. It was thought, in fact, that the acceptance of the mutability of species meant the opening of the flood gates. It was thought that this was in conflict with Scripture. Besides, it was thought that this acceptance meant that one accepts automatically also the hypotheses, theories and even the philosophy of evolutionism itself.

This had two bad results for orthodox Protestantism which even today operate with disastrous effect. In the first place, it turned its back upon the established data, giving to the pursuit of science, yes, even nature itself, a bad taste. But, in the second place, by not accepting the only point in which the idea of evolution had been proved, the philosophically strong anti-Christian evolutionist was given a weapon to brand the Christians as narrow and bigoted deniers of the facts. This is regrettable, because the Christian should be precisely the first person to show his respect for the data of creation and because centuries ago it was the Reformation that was one of the great stimulants for the investigation of nature. Above all is this regrettable because those from orthodox Protestant circles who undertook the study of natural science and realized the justification of this branding, were thus induced all the more readily to estrange themselves from the church.

This point, of the mutability of species, should have been accepted in order to combat with all the more justice unproved assertions of the evolutionists. We should learn the lesson from this that it is our duty to accept the data, no matter what problems this may raise. Similarly, the opinion that Genesis intends to convey to us something about nature in scientific terms, whether it concerns the rotation of the sun around the earth or the nature of the species, always fails and raises tensions that are detrimental to ourselves.

We should let this opinion go and at the same time we should try to eliminate from our thinking the scholastic notion about "ideas of creation."

This also means that Genesis 1 intends to impart to us something entirely different. The observant reader who has liberated his thinking from the afore-mentioned faulty presuppositions, discovers that Genesis I reveals to us something that is hidden for all experimental and formulatory science, namely, that it is God who determined which organisms there would be. At the word of God ("God said") the organisms came into existence, each after its kind. *How* they originated and *what* their nature is, of course, is not communicated. These are issues which man himself may try to discover entirely or partly, when he uses the talents that have been given to him. The main point is—and this is revealed and cannot be ascertained scientifically—that all that man can know about the origin and the nature of organisms, he can and must subject to the all-predominating influence of the determinative Word of God.

About the constancy of species of organisms, nothing is mentioned. Man himself can establish that. But also the eventual alteration in the structures of the organisms falls under the sublime discipline of the Creator of all powers of nature and of law and order in structure.

This is the mighty theme, repeated with emphasis no less than ten times in Genesis I, which does not become for the Christian biologist a depressing hindrance for his thinking and acting in the shape of disconsolately holding fast to the burden of the "constancy-of-species dogma." No, it means for him a gratefully accepted and a living reality through which he is enabled to work freely and unprejudiced with respect to modern *research*. To him it is a treasure that has been bestowed upon him and which he eagerly wishes upon all other investigators so that their thinking may be liberated from every form of cold and nihilistic determinism.

CHAPTER FIVE

THE ORIGIN OF MAN[1]

I. *Introduction*

In order to obtain a good conception of modern views concerning the problem of the origin of life and of species, we had to begin our discussion with ancient times and the Middle Ages. This is not necessary with man. It is true, since ancient times there have been thinkers who related man to the animals, but these did not have any influence upon the development of scientific research. There did not seem to be any problem here till about 1800. The general opinion was that about 6,000 or 7,000 years ago God created man in his present form. The idea of relation of descent simply did not occur to most investigators. This is illustrated clearly by the fact that Linnaeus even named the chimpanzee *Homo troglodytes* (cave-dwelling man) and combined this creature with *Homo sapiens* (wise man) into one genus. Probably he would not have done this if he had realized that later there would be

---

[1]The Editors of the monthly, *Geloof en Wetenschap*, organ of the Christelijke Vereniging van Natuur- en Geneeskundigen, in the Netherlands, have given their kind permission to use large parts of several articles on this subject which appeared in that paper.

investigators who thought that the chimpanzee was an ancestor of modern man.

Thus only a century and a half ago the tranquil assumption prevailed generally among investigators, derived from a literal interpretation of Genesis, that man was created by God only a few thousand years ago. Human fossils were not known. There was not a single argument that gave reason to suspect that it might have been different.

The situation regarding this question became entirely altered when evolutionism arose. Already in the *Philosophie Zoologique* of Lamarck of 1809 we find, next to the ideas of spontaneous generation, genetic relation of the groups of animals and mutability of species, also the view of the origin of man from the quadrupeds. This idea, which was accepted expressly by later evolutionists, was advanced by spoken and written word as such a matter of course that later the findings of the remnants of prehistoric men and of human-like beings were viewed as clear proofs for the correctness of this opinion.

Since in orthodox Protestant circles the opinion of the 18th century is usually held, partly or entirely; and, besides, the idea occurs that the acceptance of the findings of science would do great damage to Christian beliefs, we shall here enter into a more detailed discussion than in preceding chapters on the data science has gathered. This we do in order to review afterwards to what extent the first chapters of Genesis and the scientific data can be brought face to face with one another.

2. The Paleontological Findings and Their Value.

Man is classified with the mammals, more particularly with the order of Primates. Without going into all kinds of systematic details, we can divide this order into prosimians (e.g., lemurs, lorises and tarsiers), monkeys (e.g., howling monkeys, baboons, mandrills), man-apes or anthropoids (orangutan, chimpanzee, gorilla and, according to some, the gibbon) and man.[2]

---

[2] Translator's Note: It should be borne in mind that the Dutch terms "aap" and "apen" are not synonymous with their equivalents in English. Strictly speaking, the term *apes* should be confined to the higher primates. First we have the prosimians, then the monkeys, next the apes or anthropoids, then the hominoids or hominids, the human forms, to which *Homo sapiens* also belongs.

The first Primates that appeared on the earth, as far as we know at present, were prosimians (See Fig. 1). Representatives of this group have been found in the Lower-Eocene Epoch of North America, Europe and Asia; this means, from layers of the earth which are supposed to be about sixty million years old.

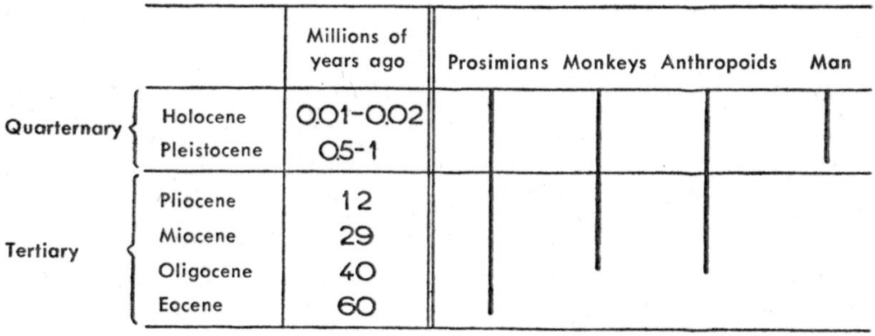

		Millions of years ago	Prosimians	Monkeys	Anthropoids	Man
Quarternary	Holocene	0.01–0.02				
	Pleistocene	0.5–1				
Tertiary	Pliocene	12				
	Miocene	29				
	Oligocene	40				
	Eocene	60				

Fig. 1

The oldest remains of *monkeys* that are known were found by the Austrian investigator Schlosser in 1910 at Fayum in Egypt in an Oligocene layer and are about thirty-five million years old. From the same epoch and in the same territory Schlosser also found remains of beings which are thought to belong to the anthropoids. That is one of the reasons why some investigators at present are of the opinion that the anthropoids did not descend from the monkeys but directly from the prosimians.[3]

The history of man carries us to the Pleistocene Epoch of the four Glacial Periods: the Günz, the Mindel, the Riss and the Würm Glacial Periods, and the three Interglacial Periods that may be differentiated between them (see Fig. 2.) To bring some order into the discussion of the many human-like fossils that are known today, we shall begin first with the discussion of those hominid forms that are best known.

During the years 1890-1892 the Netherlander Dubois (1858-1940) found at Trinil on Middle Java various fragments of a

---

[3] W. E. Le Gros Clark, *History of the Primates*, 1953, pp. 57 and 58.

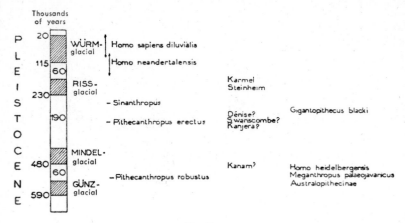

Fig. 2

being which he designated with the name *Pithecanthropus,* particularly *P. erectus,* the orthograde ape-man.[4]

The research of Dubois and the name he gave to this being have an interesting preceding history. It was Haeckel, namely, who in 1868 in his *Natürliche Schöpfungsgeschichte*[5] constructed the so-called "Pithecoid-theory" or "Affenlehre." According to this view recent man descended from the anthropoids. This happened either polyphyletically (each main race of man from one specific man-ape), or monophyletically. Haeckel gave preference to the monophyletic opinion—all the races of man have descended from one species, the "Urmensch," *Homo primigenius,* primitive man. The corollary to this opinion is that mankind also has "only one primitive homeland" where this *H. primigenius* developed himself from a kind of anthropoid long extinct. And then he writes the prophetic words: "Of the five continents existing today, neither Australia, nor America, nor Europe can be this primitive homeland or the so-called 'Paradise' or the 'cradle of the human race.' Most of the signs point much more to *South Asia.* Outside of S. Asia the only continent of today that could be called into question is Africa."[6] He then thinks particularly about so-called Lemuria,

---

[4] E. Dubois, *Pithecanthropus erectus,* eine menschenaehnliche Uebergangsform aus Java, Batavia, 1894.

[5] E. Haeckel, *Natürliche Schöpfungsgeschichte,* 3rd ed., 1872, e.g., pp. 619, 646.

[6] *Op. cit.,* p. 619.

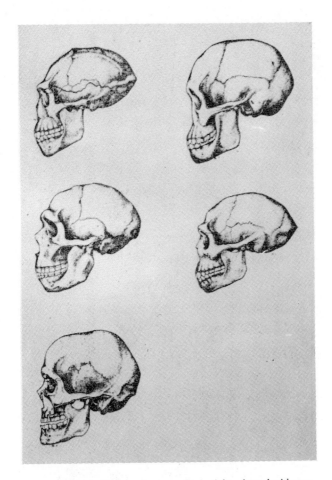

Fig. 3. Upper row: left *Pithecanthropus erectus*, right *Australopithecus;*
middle row: left *Homo neanderthalensis*, right *Sinanthropus pekinensis;*
lower: *Homo sapiens diluvialis*. (From: Romer, *Man and the Vertebrates*, 1948.)

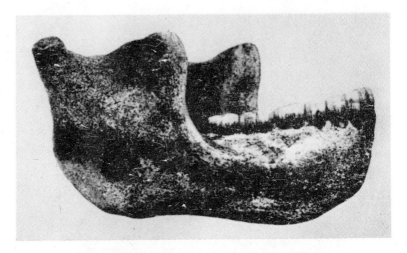

Fig. 4.   Lower jaw of *Homo heidelbergensis*.   (From: Boule et Vallois, *Les hommes fossiles*, 1952.)

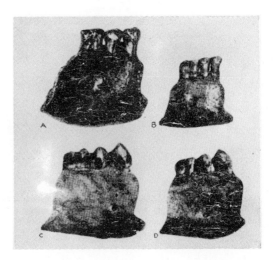

Fig. 5.   Fragments of the lower jaw of: (A) *Meganthropus paleojavanicus*, compared with corresponding pieces of lower jaw of (B) recent human, (C) a male gorilla, and (D) a male orangutan.   (From: Weidenreich, *Apes, Giants, and Man*, 1948.)

which must have extended from S. Asia and the Indian Archipelago to East Africa and Madagascar. Of this *Homo primigenius* from Lemuria no fossils were as yet known, but Haeckel could form a conception. He had a long skull with teeth that were directed forward. His hair was woolly and more compact than with us. The color of his skin was dark brown. His arms were long, his legs short and thin, his posture was semi-upright, with knees that converged inwardly. A truly articulated "Begriffssprache" (conceptual speech) this being did not yet possess. "From the mute primitive man, which we consider as the common progenitor of all other species, there developed next, probably through natural selection, various kinds of men unknown to us and long since extinct, which remained at the stage of the mute ape-man (*Alalus* [literally, without speech] or *Pithecanthropus*)."[7]

With the aid of this "compass" of Haeckel, Dubois went in search of this "*Pithecanthropus*" in S. Asia, and, as we saw, he found a fossil human-like being and he immediately connected this creature, as the name indicates, with the views of Haeckel.

We thus see here how the framework of evolutionistic thinking has influenced historical-anthropological thought. Thinkers did not confront these findings objectively, but placed them directly into phylogenetic trees, viewed them as "missing links," as "ape-men" and the like. Consistent evolutionism determined the thinking and it required a great deal of effort to liberate one's self from this.

The evolutionistic narrowness of a half century ago becomes particularly clear when expressed in Dubois' view that he had already found *the* transitional form between man-apes and man: "*Pithecanthropus erectus* is that transitional form which according to the doctrine of evolution must have existed between man and the anthropoids; he is the progenitor of man."

It is peculiar that Dubois at the end of his life changed his opinion entirely and declared that *Pithecanthropus* was a giant gibbon that only later changed abruptly into man.

In the meanwhile, however, more findings were made of the *Pithecanthropus,* particularly by the German investigator von Koenigswald (at present professor at the State University of

---
[7] *Op. cit.,* p. 621.

Utrecht), who in 1931 had accepted a position with the Geological Service of the Netherlands East Indies. About 60 km. west of Trinil, near Sangiran, in the years 1936-1939, he found remains of various other specimens of this being.

As a result of this we are at present rather well informed about the structure of the skull of these organisms (Fig. 3). This shows strong supra-orbital tori or ridges above the ocular orbits, the forehead is unusually low, the occiput has a prominent nuchal area related to the attachment of the muscles of the neck. The cranial capacity of the skulls that were found varies from 775 to fully 900 cc. The lower jaw shows no chin. If some of the femurs found by Dubois belonged indeed to Pithecanthropus, then these beings were about 1.70 m. in height.

Very interesting is the find made in 1939. This concerned, in addition to a part of the calvarium, a related fragment of the maxilla, in which can be seen clearly a space, a so-called diastema, between the canine and the lateral incisor (see Fig. 7). This find was so important because previously the view was always held that this was a typical characteristic of anthropoids. Besides, this skull is very massive in structure. Upon the basis of these particulars von Koenigswald considered this discovery to belong to a separate kind—*Pithecanthropus modjokertensis.* This is usually better known by the name given by Weidenreich *P. robustus.*

The dating of these findings caused a considerable amount of difficulty because they were discovered in secondary sedimentary deposits.[8] At present *P. erectus* is calculated to belong to the Middle Pleistocene Epoch, *P. robustus* to the Lower Pleistocene. Von Koenigswald is of the opinion that they are at least 500,000 years old.[9]

Already before von Koenigswald had started his important work in Java, the attention of anthropologists became centered upon a part of the continent of Asia, namely, near Peking. At about a distance of 65 km. from this city, in the so-called "Dragon Hill," during the years 1927-1941, remains were found of about 40 individuals of a being which morphologically seemed to be

---

[8] For a clear review of the stratigraphy of the Pliocene and Pleistocene of Java we can point to W. A. Mohler, *Experientia*, 2, pp. 287-292, 1946.

[9] G. H. R. von Koenigswald, *Die Naturwissenschaften*, 40, pp. 128-137, 1953.

strongly related to the *Pithecanthropus*. The investigations were conducted under the guidance of Davidson Black and Weidenreich. The former gave to this creature the name of *Sinanthropus pekinensis*.

The skulls of these beings (see Fig. 3)) also have massive supra-orbital tori and a protuberance in the occiput, a low forehead, although a little more elevated than that of the *Pithecanthropus*. The cranial capacity, accordingly, was also greater and varied, according to Weidenreich,[10] from 850-1300 cc., and according to von Koenigswald,[11] from 915-1225 cc. Also the *Sinanthropus* had no chin. They were relatively small, the males about 156 cm., the females about 144 cm. in height. This means that they were about as large as the present Eskimos, Japanese, Bushmen, and the like.

By many investigators *Sinanthropus* is placed in the Middle Pleistocene Epoch, more particularly in the Mindel-Riss Inter-glacial Period (see Fig. 2). Hence, he lived about 250,000-450,000 years ago.[12]

The following important group forms the Neanderthalers. In August 1856 there was found in the Feldhofer Grotte in the Neander valley, a short distance from Düsseldorf, Germany, a fairly complete skeleton that showed a number of exceptional characteristics: the skull was somewhat coarsely constructed, with massive supraorbital tori, forming an uninterrupted shelf of bone overhanging the orbits, the forehead slanting backwards. Thus, in its entirety it deviated rather strongly from the skeleton of recent man. One should realize that until that time there never had been found a skeleton that deviated from the recent human type. Yet, there soon were investigators who knew how to evaluate this finding. The Irish anatomist King in 1864 called him *Homo neanderthalensis* and considered him to be a prehistoric man. Lyell visited the place of discovery in 1868 and determined that the find was from the Pleistocene Epoch. Huxley thought that the Neanderthaler was the most ape-like man that he had ever seen.

---

[10] F. Weidenreich, *Apes, Giants and Man*, 4th ed., 1948, p. 93.

[11] G. H. R. von Koeningswald, *op cit.*, 1953, p. 131.

[12] See for an extensive discussion of the *Pithecanthropus and Sinanthropus* forms: J. P. Kleiweg de Zwaan, *De oudste mensheid in Europa en Indonesië* The Hague, 1955.

There were also vehement opponents. Thus Rudolph Virchow thought the skeleton was derived from a recent human who had suffered from rickets or arthritis and whose skull had been severely damaged during his life. Others opined that they were remains of a Mongolian Cossack of the Russian army of 1814, or of an old Hollander, a poor Irishman, a fugitive savage, and the like.

This conflict lasted until 1901 when Schwalbe and Klaatsch, partly on the basis of a few other specimens that had been found in the meanwhile, established the general opinion that we were dealing here with a separate being who should be viewed as primitive man.

Through a great number of findings our knowledge about these beings has been greatly extended. At present there are at our disposal no less than almost 200 specimens of individuals found in Spain, France, Belgium, Germany, Italy, Jugoslavia, the Crimea and Uzbekistan. Besides, outside of this area, there are Neanderthaloid forms known from Palestine, S. Africa and Java.

This *Homo neanderthalensis* was about of the same size as the *Sinanthropus,* the males about 160 cm., the females 145 cm. The cranial capacity was large, varying from about 1200 to nearly 1650 cc. When we think of the fact that the average cranial capacity of recent man is 1350 cc., we see why various investigators came to the conclusion that on the average the Neanderthalers possessed more brains than we do.

The skull (see Fig. 3) is strikingly long and fairly flat, the supra-orbital tori are strongly developed, the jaws are extended, animal-like, in the form of a snout.

The strikingly high occipital protuberance is an indication that the skull was carried fairly well forward. The arms are, comparatively speaking, longer than with us. The femur shows a curvature so that, when standing, the creature appeared knock-kneed.

These Neanderthalers lived in the last part of the Riss-Würm Interglacial Period and at the beginning of the Würm Glacial Period (see Fig. 2). This means fully 150,000 to 60-70,000 years ago.

The last main group which we must discuss constitutes man of the last Ice Age: *Homo sapiens diluvialis*. The first remains of this creature were found in 1860 by E. Lartet at the little town of Aurignac in France. At present there are remains of about 180 individuals which were found over an extensive area of the Old World: France, Germany, Czechoslovakia, Siberia, the Crimea, North, East, and South Africa, China, Java and Australia.

The structure of these men corresponds with ours in large measure (see Fig. 3): high forehead, the occiput rounded, slightly developed supra-orbital tori, a chin. They had a large cranial capacity, sometimes more than 1700 cc. (Chancelade); they were about as tall as we, with corresponding racial differences.

As far as dating is concerned, they lived during the Würm Glacial Period (see Fig. 2). They are estimated to have lived from 60,000 - 100,000 to 10,000 - 20,000 years ago.

We have now discussed the four human-like groups about which we have the best information: *Pithecanthropus, Sinanthropus, Homo neanderthalensis* and *Homo sapiens diluvialis*. The next question we can ask is whether there is any occasion to suppose that there existed a genetic relation between these groups. That we, *Homo sapiens recens* descended from *Homo sapiens diluvialis* must be accepted. The relation between the latter and the other human-like forms, however is not so clear.

It is easily understood that initially it was surmised that *Homo sapiens diluvialis* descended from *Homo neanderthalensis*, the latter from *Sinanthropus* and *Pithecanthropus*, and these again from anthropoids, such as the chimpanzee.

During the last decades the picture of our genealogical tree is beginning to alter appreciably in different respects. This modification concerns itself in the first place with the relation between *Homo sapiens diluvialis* and *Homo neanderthalensis*. With the dating of the individual findings, it appeared first of all that the Neanderthalers did not always have the same structure, but rather, that the typical Neanderthaloid features developed themselves ever more strongly in the course of time. It seems, therefore, that these beings have developed themselves in a constantly more specialized direction. This tendency to specialize brings with it that it is very improbable that *Homo sapiens* originated from the Neanderthaler.

In the second place—and this emphasizes strongly what we have just conveyed—many investigators have come to the conclusion that it is exactly the oldest Neanderthaloid specimens we know that possess characteristics strikingly resembling those of *Homo sapiens*. To these belong, for example, the skull which was found in 1933 by Berckhemer at Steinheim, 30 km. north of Stuttgart, and a large number (15-20) skeletons which were exhumed by Miss Garod and MacCown in 1931 and 1932 in the caves Et Tabun and Mugharet es Skhul in Mt. Carmel, and by Neuville and Stékelis in the cave of Djebel Kafzeh near Nazareth.[13]

One can interpret these interesting findings in different ways (see Fig. 2). For example, they may have reference to crossings between *Homo sapiens* and *H. neanderthalensis,* or *H. neanderthalensis* developed from *H. sapiens,* or, these remains stand at the bifurcation of both forms.

Whatever opinion one favors, all imply that the direct *sapiens*-line is at least just as old as that of *H. neanderthalensis.* In addition, if it is correct that various investigators place these mixed skulls in the Riss Glacial Period[14] or in the second Interglacial,[15] then one can conclude that the *sapiens*-line goes back to more than 200,000 years.

This in itself is already an important conclusion. Of still greater significance is the fact that during the last half century various findings have been made of *sapiens*-like skulls which many authors consider to be still older. This concerns the skull fragments of Swanscombe (England), Dénise (France), and Kanam and Kanjera (Africa) (see Fig. 2). (In the same series of mysterious forms the Piltdown man was also included, who, as was revealed a few years ago, was a falsification.) If it is correct that Dénise, Swanscombe and Kanjera can be placed in the Second Interglacial Period, and Kanam even in the First Interglacial or in

---

[13] M. Boule, et H. V. Vallois, *Les hommes fossiles,* Paris, 1952, 4th ed., p. 175ff., p. 392ff.

[14] H. Weinert, *Stammesentwicklung der Menschheit,* Braunschweig, 1951, p. 147.

[15] J. Kälin, *Experientia,* 3, pp. 272-287, 1946.

the Günz-Glacial, then it would be a remarkable consequence that the representatives of the *sapiens*-group were at least contemporaries of *Sinanthropus* and *Pithecanthropus* and perhaps even lived before them. This would mean, besides, that *H.* *sapiens* is not descended from *Sinanthropus* and *Pithecanthropus,* but that, if any mention is to be made of genetic relationship, the possibility should be considered whether the last-named are not the progeny of the *sapiens*-forms.

These ideas find an expert defender in the Swiss Kälin.[16] The view of Leakey,[17] finder of the Kanam and Kanjera fragments, deviates even farther from current opinions. He holds the view that the *sapiens*-line goes back even to the Miocene Epoch and that all other human-like finds (Neanderthalers, *Sinanthropus, Pithecanthropus* and the giant-forms to be considered soon) belong to an entirely different branch which descended out of the Miocene Epoch.

These interesting, but not at all sufficiently founded ideas, have been robbed more or less of their anti-evolutionistic sting by a hypothetical construction of Weidenreich.[18] This investigator has advanced the idea that we should not suppose that there is only one genetic line that runs to recent man, which then only recently disintegrated into various races, but that a number of lines are to be distinguished which at times may all or not have been in contact with one another. In each one of these lines the corresponding stages are passed (e.g., *Pithecanthropus,* Neanderthaler, *H. sapiens*). One can suppose that the tempo could vary. Thus in one line the *sapiens*-stage could have been reached, while another still was at an older stage morphologically.

This view of Weidenreich, which, if correct, in truth gives an explanation of the *sapiens*-findings mentioned, contains yet a second interesting aspect. Weidenreich thinks that each of these lines begins with a giant-stage. And indeed, during this century

[16] J. Kälin, 1946, *op. cit.;* "Die ältesten Menschenreste und ihre Stammesgeschichtliche Deutung," *Historia Mundi* I, p. 79ff., 1952; See also S. Cole, *The Prehistory of East Africa,* London, 1954, p. 80.

[17] L. S. B. Leakey, *Adam's Ancestors,* London, 1953, pp. 200-212.

[18] F. Weidenreich, *op. cit.,* 1948, p. 30.

various findings have been made of probably very large human-like beings.

The first concerns a lower jaw (see Fig. 4) which in 1907 was dug up by Mauer in the vicinity of Heidelberg.[19] This remnant of the *Homo heidelbergensis* lay in a sedimentary deposit which belongs to the Günz-Mindel Interglacial Period and which is accepted to be more than 400,000 years old. Looking at the structure and the arrangement of the teeth and molars and the general form of the jaw, it must be considered human-like.

Striking are the size and the thickness of this jaw (at the level of the last molar 23 mm., in the case of *Homo sapiens* maximally 14 mm.). A chin is missing.

A second giant find concerns two lower jaw fragments found by von Koenigswald in 1936 and 1941 near Sangiran on Java and named by him *Meganthropus palaeojavanicus.*[20] These jaw fragments excel in size and thickness (26.6 mm.) all known jaws of fossil and recent man and anthropoids (see Fig. 5). Also these jaws show many strikingly human-like features. They belong to the Lower Pleistocene Epoch.

Von Koenigswald discovered in the years 1935 and 1939 in China some teeth and molars (see Fig. 6) which have still larger measurements and which he ascribes to the form *Gigantopithecus blacki.*[21] The molars have a crown area three times as large as ours. Weidenreich, upon the basis of the size of these molars, has calculated that the lower jaw of these beings must have been 18 cm. long and 5.5 cm. high with a thickness of almost 3.5 cm. (cf. the earlier enumerated values). This means twice as long, 2.5 times as thick, and 1.75 as high as the lower jaw of *Homo sapiens recens.* According to Weidenreich—but there is some cause for criticism[22] —the size of this human-like being, if he was proportioned as we are, would have been 4.5 m. in height, weight about 400-600 kg.

Also in East-Africa, in 1939, a large fragment of an upper jaw was found, named by Weinert *Meganthropus africanus.*[23] How-

[19] O. Schoetensack, *Der Unterkiefer des Homo heidelbergensis,* Leipzig, 1908.
[20] G. H. R. von Koenigswald, *Studies in Physical Anthropology,* I, pp. 83-98, 1949.
[21] G. H. R. von Koenigswald, *Anthr. Papers,* Amer. Mus. Nat. Hist., 43, pp. 295-325, 1952.
[22] H. Weinert, 1951, *op. cit.,* p. 97.
[23] H. Weinert, 1951, *op. cit.,* p. 101ff.

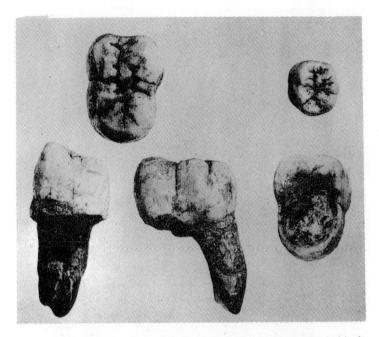

Fig. 6. Pictured on the same scale, a few molars of *Gigantopithecus blacki* (the four large specimens), and a molar of recent man (the small item, upper right). (From: Von Koenigswald, *Anthropological Papers of the American Museum of Natural History*, 43, 295–325, 1952.)

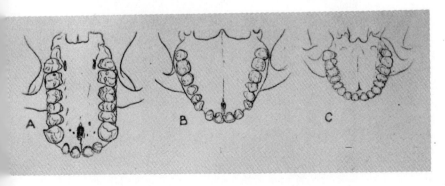

Fig. 7. Upper jaws of: (A) gorilla, (B) *Pithecanthropus robustus*, (C) recent man. (From: Weidenreich, *Apes, Giants and Man*, 1948)

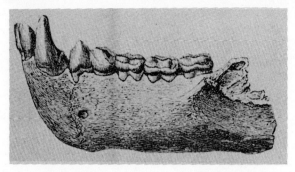

Fig. 8. Lower jaw of a fossil anthropoid. (From Boule et Vallois, *Les hommes fossiles*, 1952.)

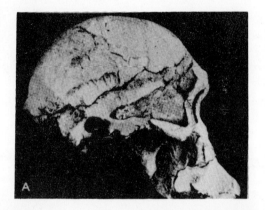

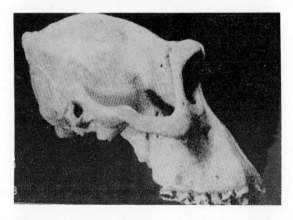

Fig. 9. (A) a skull from one of the *Australopithecinae;* (B) for comparison, the skull of a female gorilla. (From: Le Gros Clark, *History of the Primates*, 1953.)

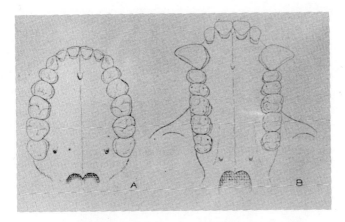

Fig. 10. (A) upper jaw of the skull of an *Australopithecus;* (B) of the skull of a gorilla.   (From: Le Gros Clark, *History of the Primates*, 1953.)

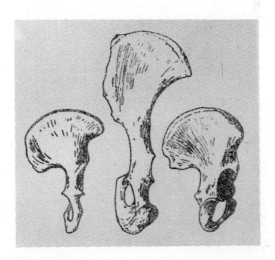

Fig. 11. The right pelvic girdle (left to right) of an *Australopithecus*, of a male chimpanzee, and of a recent human.   (From Kramp, in *Schöpfungsglaube und Evolutionstheorie*, 1955.)

Fig. 13. Stone implements from the Kafuan Period of East Africa. (From: Cole, *The Prehistory of East Africa*, 1954.)

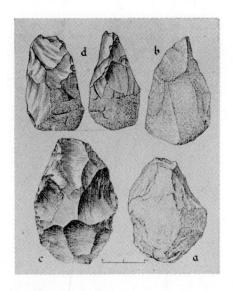

Fig. 14. Hand-axes from the Abbevillian Period of: (a) East Africa, (b) Morocco, (c) France, (d) England. (From: Oakley, *Man the Toolmaker*, 1952.)

ever, the possibility has been offered that this form belongs to the Australopithecinae, soon to be discussed.[24]

All the giant forms that have been mentioned belong to the Middle and Lower Pleistocene Epoch and they are, therefore, very old. When Weidenreich reviewed these findings it made him reminisce that *P. robustus,* which was older than *P. erectus,* was also heavily built. This indicated, according to him, that the older the findings, the larger was the build of the human-like beings. He was induced to construct a phylogenetic tree: *Gigantopithecus, Meganthropus P. robustus, P. erectus* etc., in whom the size of the body successively decreased.[25] Thus, according to Weidenreich, mankind descended from giants. Von Koenigswald[26] has made it probable that Weidenreich incorrectly placed *Gigantopithecus* in this series. In the first place, the molars of this creature are too specialized for man to have descended from this being, but in addition, upon geological and paleontological grounds, it must be granted that *Gigantopithecus* was a contemporary of *Sinanthropus* (see Fig. 2) and thus definitely cannot be placed at the beginning of the series. For the rest also von Koenigswald is of the opinion that the oldest human-like forms were giants.

In the preceding we have repeatedly designated molars, jaws and skulls by the term "human-like." And indeed there are some anatomical characteristics of the skeleton in which recent man clearly differs from the recent anthropoids.[27] We shall review a few of these briefly:

1. In the first place the curvature of the jaws in man forms a wide symmetrically divergent arcade (see Fig. 7), while in the anthropoids the molars appear in fairly well parallel rows, with a pronounced arch near the canines.

2. In the second place, the human canines are never fangs; they hardly protrude beyond the rows of teeth, or not at all (see Fig. 8).

---

[24] G. H. R. von Koenigswald, 1953, *op. cit.,* p. 132.

[25] F. Weidenreich, *op. cit.,* 1948; *Studies in Phys. Anthr.,* 1, pp. 149-157, 1949.

[26] G. H. R. von Koenigswald, 1952, *op. cit.*

[27] It is interesting to compare the different evaluations of the resemblances and contrasts of the bodily structure of men and anthropoids. Cf., e.g., H. Weinert, *Ursprung der Menschheit,* Stuttgart, 1944, with A. H. Schulz, *Cold Spring Harbor Symposia on Quant. Biol.,* 15, 1950, pp. 37-53, and F. Weidenreich, *Apes,* etc., 1948, *op. cit.,* p. 5ff.

3. Thirdly, with man the first lower premolar never possesses a sharp blade, as occurs with the anthropoids, where this forms a scissor with the upper-canine (see Fig. 8).

4. A fourth complex of characteristics concerns itself with the typical upright stature of man. Among other things, this has important results for structure of the pelvis and, in regard to the anthropoids, the forward displacement of the foramen magnum.

These four human-like attributes together with various others have been found back in all the forms that have been discussed (in so far as the fragments possessed the items of the skeletal parts concerned). That is why they were designated by the term "human-like."

But particularly after the last World War remains were found in South Africa of some very peculiar beings, due to which these distinguishing features lost their value to a large extent as criteria for being "human."

The first skull of the organisms we have in mind was found in 1924 in the district of Taungs, about 120 km. north of Kimberley. He was investigated by Dart, who gave him the name *Australopithecus africanus*. In 1936 near Sterkfontein, about 55 km. west of Johannesburg, a second skull was found. Broom called this one *Australopithecus transvaalensis*, afterwards *Plesianthropus transvaalensis*. In 1938, near Kromdraai, also in the vicinity of Johannesburg, a skull was found of somewhat more robust construction. Hence, Broom attached to it the name *Paranthropus robustus*. In April, 1947, near Sterkfontein, a second skull was found of *Plesianthropus*, in 1948 a pelvis. In the same year there were unearthed near Swartkrans remains of a giant-form, *Paranthropus crassidens*. In 1947 and 1948 Dart found, much farther north near Makapan, remains of a form that was called *Australopithecus prometheus*. And since that time many new findings have been made, for example, in 1953 five skulls.

Thus today we have at our disposal a few score specimens by means of which we can form a fairly good impression of these organisms (see Fig. 9).

These beings had a cranial capacity which most authors estimate between 450 and 800 cc.[28] This means that they had less than half the cranial capacity that we have. Hence, as far as this character is concerned, they belong in the order of the size of recent anthropoids (gorilla maximally about 685 cc.). The jaws are massively built, the molars are forceful.

In addition to these and other anthropoid-like features, these *Australopithecinae* display a staggering number of human-like features. Thus with most of them (with the exception of *Paranthropus crassidens*) the muscle ridges on the skull are much less developed than in recent anthropoids, the forehead is arched, the supraorbital tori do not form a shelf above the eyes, the foramen magnum is situated fairly well forward in the base of the cranium, the occiput gives a human-like impression. The teeth are particularly human-like (Fig. 10). The rows of molars diverge and slope into the teeth, the canines do not protrude outside of the row, the lower anterior premolar lacks every indication of a scissor-function.

Not only the skull, but also the bones of the limbs display strong human-like features. According to many this points to the possibility of a vertical posture. A similar indication is the position of the foramen magnum, but particularly the structure of the pelvis, which is surprisingly human (see Fig. 11).

Thus the skeletons of these *Australopithecinae* have such a mixture of anthropoid-like and human-like features that they excel all that which one has ever dared to expect concerning "missing-links."

Although initially it was thought that traces of cultural expressions of these beings had been observed (weapons from bones, use of fire), during recent years there has been a nearly unanimous retreat because none of these could stand the test of criticism.[29] According to most authors, in all likelihood they were not humans, but animals.

Naturally, it is of great importance where in geological time these *Australopithecinae* should be placed. At present this is a

---

[28] F. Weidenreich, *Scientific Monthly*, 67, p. 103, 1948; G. H. R. von Koenigswald, 1953, *op. cit.*, p. 134.
[29] In a recent book Dart defended again the primitive culture of these beings: R. Dart. *The Osteodontokeratic Culture of Australopithecus Prometheus*, Pretoria, 1957.

point of great controversy. Many authors (for example Boule, Le Gros Clark, Heberer and Hooton)[30] think that there are indications that they lived not only at the beginning of the Pleistocene Epoch, but that they lived already at the end of the Pliocene Epoch that preceded it. Others (for instance, von Koenigswald) have adduced important arguments which plead for the hypothesis that they belonged to the Pleistocene Epoch and were comtemporaries of the *Pithecanthropus* forms (see Fig. 2).[31]

Von Koenigswald and Weidenreich are therefore not inclined to take them up directly in our genealogical tree. According to them they are side-branches of it and they possess the human-like characters only because they inherited them from a hypothetical progenitor which they had in common with man. They were the animal representatives in the group of those that were human-like.[32]

These findings surprised the anthropologists very much. The cause of this surprise lies in this that it shows clearly that we did not rescend from recent anthropoids or from beings that resembled them very much. Besides, the findings indicate that the typically human features are much older than we ever imagined. Or, as Kälin expresses it: "The sensational aspect lies much more in this, that in the view of the biologists the image of man appears more and more human-like and that the expression of his bodily independence in animal ancestry from the higher Primates has been largely removed. Instead of the brutal, animal-like primitive man, as he lived in the fantasy of Ernst Haeckel, we have today a picture of man from whose countenance since his earliest existence issues the breath of the spirit."[33]

In review it thus appears from what has been discussed, that from the beginning of the Pleistocene Epoch we know various human-like forms. When we now presuppose for a moment, in anticipation of the conclusion which we shall soon formulate, that

[30] M. Boule et H. V. Valois, *op. cit.*, p. 92: Le Gros Clark, *op. cit.*, p. 65; G. Heberer, *Neue Ergebnisse der menschlichen Abstammungslehre*, 1951, p. 57; E. A. Hooton, *Up From the Ape*, 1946, p. 281.
[31] G. H. R. von Koenigswald, *Proc. Kon. Ned. Akad. v. Wetensch.* Series B, 56, pp. 403-413, 427-438, 1953; 57, 85-91, 1954; *Nature*, 173, p. 795, 1954. See also A. S. Romer, *Man and the Vertebrates*, 7th ed., 1948, p. 187.
[32] See for an opposite point of view: F. Falkenburger, *Actes du IVe Congrès International des Sciences Anthr. et Ethn. I*, 105-106, 1954.
[33] J. Kälin, 1952, *op. cit.*, p. 96.

during the entire Pleistocene Epoch there appeared human beings
on the earth, then it is important for us to ask what is known about
the time before the Pleistocene, because, of course, the origin of
man then should be sought there. And then we must state that
it is very peculiar that from the entire Pliocene Epoch no remains
of beings are known that could be considered the ancestors of man.
Since von Koenigswald has shown that *Gigantopithecus* and a few
fossil findings of orangutans from Asia should be placed in the
Pleistocene and has made it very probable that the *Australopithecinae* also date from that Epoch, there are no longer any undisputed
anthropoid fossils from the Pliocene.[34] Only from the preceding
Miocene Epoch are there again anthropoids (Dryopithecinae,
Proconsul and the like). There is before the Pleistocene a period
of 10 to 15 million years from which nothing is known about the
eventual human genealogical tree.

Heberer, who considers that the *Australopithecinae* ("Praehomininen") are very closely allied to the human genealogical tree,
speaks about this gap as follows: "Here the fossil tradition still
fails us entirely. Between the proconsuloid types and the South
African "Praehomininen," the 'transitional area from animal to
man,' there stretches itself over 15 million years a chain of 'missing
links.' . . . ."[35]

This means that if the *Australopithecinae* do not belong to our
ancestors and that if in the Lower Pleistocene there were already
living human beings, then absolutely nothing is known about the
origin of man.[36] The opinion expressed at times, that it has been
proved that man descended from anthropoids, lacks a scientific
basis.

This expression would be too bold if we had at our disposal
only fossil material of which we discussed the most important in
the foregoing. Because is not already the mingling of human-like
and anthropoid features which, for example, we met in *Pithecanthropus,* proof that man only at the beginning of the Pleistocene

---

[34] Cf. M. Boule et H. V. Vallois, *op. cit.*, p. 86.
[35] G. Heberer, *op. cit.*, p. 71.
[36] Interesting is the idea of M. Westenhöfer (*Die Grundlagen meiner Theorie
vom Eigenweg des Menschen,* Heidelberg, 1948) that the separate human line
goes back at least to the first time the mammals appeared. Also for this
opinion there are no records that can be adduced.

Epoch liberated himself from the entwining of the anthropoid stem?

To answer this question we have to change to another subject. Investigators are becoming more and more convinced that upon the basis of the remnants of skeletons of these old forms it is not possible to decide whether a being is man or animal.

Le Gros Clark says that the only way out of the dilemma is that "probably the definition of 'Man' will ultimately have to rest on a functional rather than an anatomical basis, the criteria of humanity being the ability to speak and make tools."[37]

This means that the structure of the skeleton does not give an answer to our question, but the products of the human spiritual capacities do. This expression of Le Gros Clark fits entirely into the framework of our line of thought in the discussion of the problem of species, where it was established that the individuality-structure of the behavior of animals in connection with the characterizing of species is of the utmost importance. The direction in which historical anthropological investigation is developing is an indication of the correctness of this opinion. This speaks for itself when as morphological criteria for the human form there is selected the structure of the pelvis, of teeth or molars. Many are not convinced that the shape and the size of the brain, the seat of the "spiritual structures," are valueless for us as criteria. For many investigators the cranial capacity still plays an important role as the last remaining anatomical skeletal criterium.

Since we all are inclined to view the possession of a large brain as a sign of intelligence, it will be a good thing to consider this criterium for a moment. Weidenreich posed the following question: "Is modern man really more intelligent than Peking or Java man or any great ape only because his brain is larger?"[38] We shall consider his answer to this question. Recent man has a cranial capacity of about 1350 cc. More interesting, however, are the minimum and the maximum values, which are plus-minus 910 and plus-minus 2100 cc.[39] An extensive investigation has brought to light that human beings with a small brain definitely do not

---

[37] W. E. Le Gros Clark, 1952, *op. cit.*, p. 73.
[38] F. Weidenreich, "The Human Brain in the Light of its Phylogenetic Development," *Scientific Monthly*, 67, pp. 103-109, 1948.
[39] F. Weidenreich, *Apes*, etc., 1948, *op. cit.*, p. 92.

have to be less intelligent than those with a large brain. There
is no reason to suppose that Anatole France, Gambetta and Justus
von Liebig, who possessed brains of only 1100 cc., were inferior
in intelligence to Cuvier with a brain of 1860 cc. or Cromwell,
Lord Byron, Jonathan Swift or Turgeniev with 2,000 or more.[40]
According to Frieling the recent Australian natives and the Bushmen have only about 900 cc.

The minimum values of recent man thus fit in the order of size of
Sinanthropus and *Pithecanthropus* (Fig. 12).

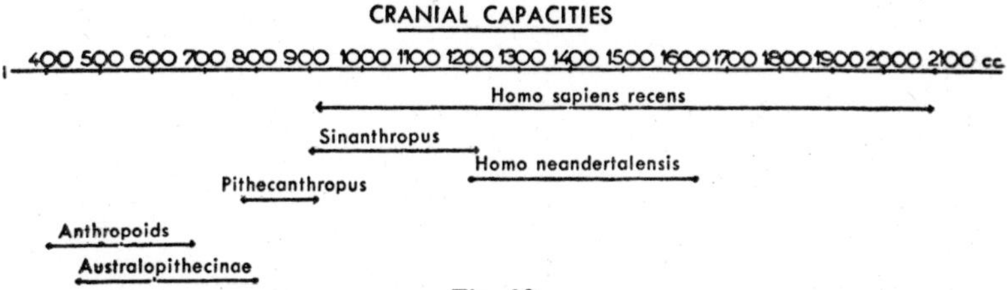

CRANIAL CAPACITIES

Fig. 12

Weidenreich concludes that "neither the absolute nor the relative
size of the brain can be used to measure the degree of mental
ability in animal or in man." At the end of the article concerned
he comes to the conclusion, "studies made on skeletons alone will
never enable us to make statements about either the mentality of
the individuals concerned or about mental change or progress over
a period of time." How can this then be done? "Cultural objects
are the only guide so far as spiritual life is concerned."

This means that along the anatomical way we cannot come to
the conclusion what is still animal or is already man, and thus
cannot determine how old humanity is. We can only come to a
nearer solution of the problem by the use of the material evidences
of the highest activities of man.

3. *The Cultural Relics*

Thus we next shall have to give briefly a description of the
cultural development of man.[41]

---

[40] These data are partly derived from H. Frieling, *Was ist der Mensch?*,
Bamberg, 1948.
[41] See about this, *e.g.*: K. P. Oakley, *Man the Toolmaker*, London, 1952;
L. S. B. Leakey, *op. cit.*, H. Kühn, *Das Erwachen der Menschheit*, Frankfurt, 1954; *Eiszeitmalerei*, München, 1956; and for the Mesolithicum, etc.:
Die Kunst Alteuropas, Stuttgart, 1954; *Der Aufstieg der Menschheit*, Frankfurt,
1955.

The oldest stone implements have been found in Africa. The people that made them dwelled along the banks of rivers and the shores of lakes, dependent as these people were upon water and wildlife. They made the tools from the boulders they found on bank and shore. These tools were extremely primitive in shape (see Fig. 13). By striking off two or three flakes at one end they obtained a sharp edge or a simple point.

These tools were used supposedly to skin the prey and to cut pieces of flesh. We know about this type of industry from East Africa, the Sudan, the Belgian Congo and from a terrace of the river Vaal in South Africa.

The interesting finding is that these oldest-known human cultural products date from the Lower Pleistocene Epoch. One has to conclude, therefore, that the humans concerned were contemporaries of the Australopithecinae. This includes that, if our chronology is correct, man occurred upon this earth already about 500,000 years ago.

Somewhat more recent, but not much more developed, are tools found in Tanganyika.

After these pebble-tool cultures there followed in the First Interglacial Period the hand-axe cultures. These tools demonstrate an advanced stage: much larger parts of the surface of the stone were struck off with the aid of a hammer stone, because of which deep scars appeared (see Fig. 14).

It is supposed that this culture began in Central Africa, possibly in connection with the pebble-tool cultures, and that in the course of a few tens of thousands of years it spread over the larger part of Africa to Western Europe and South Asia.

These hand-axe cultures existed for a long period of time. Thus we know them, for example, also from the Second Interglacial Period of Western Europe. About the same time there were territories to the north and the east where other cultures appeared.

If one accepts that the earliest human beings lived in Central Africa, then they must have expanded very rapidly to Eastern Asia, because also there very old and primitive implements have been found. Very old are the tools found in the habitat of the *Sinanthropus* and they possibly were manufactured by himself.

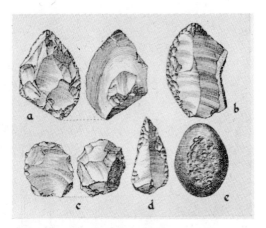

Fig. 15. Implements from the Mousterian Period (the culture of the Neanderthalers) of France (a, b, c, d); and Gibraltar (e, a hammerstone). (From:
Oakley, *Man the Toolmaker*, 1952.)

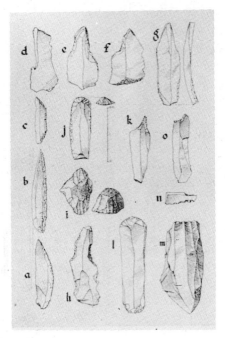

Fig. 16. Implements of *Homo sapiens diluvialis* from France, *e.g.*, (a and b) small
knives; (d and e) etching tools; (k) a drill; (n) a small saw. (From:
Oakley, *Man the Toolmaker*, 1952.)

Fig. 17. A "double-burial" of *Homo sapiens diluvialis*, of a young man and an older woman. Notice the pronouncedly flexed position, the bracelets of the woman and the snail-shell head-ornaments of the man. (From Boule et Vallois, *Les hommes fossiles*, 1952.)

They are made of boulders and of other weathered pieces of stone; and have a very crude shape with only little secondary retouching. There was, however, already in use the anvil and the hammer stone.

In Java, from layers that are somewhat more recent than those that contained the *Pithecanthropus erectus,* stone implements have been found that resemble very much those found in China.

From about the same time, namely, from the beginning of the Second Glacial Period and after that, stone implements are known from England and Central and Eastern Europe. From all this one gets the impression that already in the Lower Pleistocene Epoch and at the beginning of the Middle Pleistocene, hence about 400,000 years ago, man inhabited virtually the whole Old World.

Almost unnoticed, in the preceding, we have called the beings that made the tools, "humans." The reason for this is that a zoologist cannot conceive of an animal that is able to make implements that have been manufactured according to a definite plan and with a definite purpose. It would take a detailed exposition to make this acceptable to every reader. Perhaps we can lead some along a different road to the conclusion that man is already hundreds of thousands of years old. From the same sedimentary layers in the Dragon Hill near Peking in which the *Sinanthropus* remains were found (which are supposed to be 250,000-450,000 years old) there have also been discovered small, soft black layers containing little pieces of charred wood and charred bones. Also found were layers of ash which chemical analysis showed contained free carbon. Hence, we deal here with fireplaces where meat was roasted. Under and between these black layers were small layers of red and yellow clay which are the baked remains from the bottom of the hearth. In the layers of ashes were found partly burned bones that came from horses, bison, rhinoceros and other animals which lived in the vicinity of Peking in the hoary past. In the same layers occurred the implements named. The burning of fire and the roasting of flesh are impossible for an animal. To the contrary, animals are mortally afraid of fire. Only man can make and control it.

Passing by various other cultures from the Middle Pleistocene Epoch, we meet next the culture of the Neanderthalers. Specific

for this are, among others (see Fig. 15), a D-formed cutting tool
and a sharp point. They show a much farther advanced, although
still coarse, retouching than the former industries of which we
spoke. Very striking is the fact that, at least as far as we know,
neither the Neanderthaler nor his predecessors employed bone to
fabricate "wrought" tools.

After the culture of the Neanderthalers there followed that of
Homo sapiens diluvialis during the Last Glacial Period. According
to Oakley their culture had its beginning in Southwest Asia, perhaps in the neighborhood of Iran, from where it spread virtually
over the whole Old World.[42] (Probably only at the end of the Last
Glacial Period did man cross the Bering Straits and emigrate
for the first time to America. The oldest findings in America are
about 10,000 to 20,000 years old.)

The most characteristic differences from the preceding periods are
the very uniform stone implements made of narrow parallel-sided
flakes with a fine retouching of the edges (see Fig. 16). Further,
the hand-axes, e.g., are lacking and for the first time there appear
implements of bone, antlers and horn.

Without going into the different phases which can be clearly
differentiated in the types of tools of *Homo sapiens diluvialis*,
Glacial Man, it must be pointed out that during the Last Glacial
Period there took place, as it were, an explosive development of
human culture. We know typically shaped stone knives, ivory
awls, spearpoints of stone and horn, harpoons, needles with
an eye, engraved needle-cases sometimes with needles still in
them, lamps, forklike tools, but also, for example, flutes of one or
more notes, fabricated from bone. Next to that, armbands, rings,
head ornaments of shells, pretty stones, perforated shells of snails
and teeth, of amber and horn. They also already saved fossils.

Remarkable it is that many of these objects were discovered in
places that were thousands of kilometers removed from where
they were originally, so that we have to accept the fact that these
people carried on commerce and traveled over great distances.
Thus, there are found in Switzerland shells derived from the
Atlantic Ocean, but also, for example, ammonites (cephalopods)
from Bavaria, Austria and the vicinity of Bordeaux. Also known

---

[42] K. P. Oakley, 1952, *op. cit.*, pp. 56ff.

are great camps of *H. Sapiens diluvialis* with remnants of huts and storage places.[43]

Further, it is common knowledge that man of the Ice Age also engraved bone and ivory very artistically. Besides, he made many drawings and oil paintings in the caves. In the same places have been found scores of small images, particularly of women, but also of males and animals.[44]

When we survey these phases of culture we become deeply impressed with the enormous development of the technical know-how of man during the Pleistocene Epoch, and especially during the last ice age.

This has been viewed as a proof of an evolution of the "spiritual capacities." Initially man with his stone implements was little more than an animal and gradually, together with an increase of the size of the brain, the "spiritual structures" developed, it is said.

When we think of the fact that we do not consider our ancestors of 150 years ago, who were not able to fabricate radios, airplanes and railroads, as less intelligent that we are, then we see that the cultural development of man is of an entirely different nature than that of a biotic evolution. We are dealing here with an historical unfolding, based on discoveries and tradition. Thus it is not inconceivable, even probable, that early Pleistocene man was not mentally inferior to recent man.

4. *The Religion of Prehistoric Man*

Since in the next section we shall consider the relation of scientific findings to Genesis, it is of great importance to review before that briefly whether investigators have obtained facts that demonstrate a religious consciousness of the Pleistocene human forms.[45]

Three aspects which can be distinguished in every religion will be discussed at this time: the attitude concerning the hereafter, the cult, and the idea they had of God.

About the attitude in regard to the *hereafter,* something can be derived from the manner in which the dead were treated.

---

[43] R. C. Andrews, *Apen, schedels en mensen,* Rotterdam, 1952, pp. 172ff.
[44] Cf. *e.g.,* J. Maringer and H. G. Bandi, *Art in the Ice Age,* Basle, 1953.
[45] Cf. also: E. O. James, *Prehistoric Religion,* London, 1957.

Of the oldest human-like forms, such as *Pithecanthropus* and *Sinanthropus,* the skeletal remains are usually found sadly mutilated. Very generally the base of the skull around the foramen magnum is broken open, supposedly in order to consume the brains. Probably cannibalism was widespread. However, it is important that already among the Neanderthalers we find real graves. A number of these people were buried in shallow graves, with the legs sharply flexed, while stones were placed around the body for protection. In the graves, stone implements and pieces of meat were placed along side. In addition, the corpse was besprinkled with red ocher.

Such graves were not common among the Neanderthalers and, significantly, their remains have also been found among the offal; but, by the time of the ice age man, burial is a rule (see Fig. 17). Also their graves were made in the inhabited cave, often in the ashes of the hearth. In this the corpse, covered with red ocher, was placed with sharply flexed knees, together with implements, adornments and food. Stones formed a protection around the whole. This method of burial was a practice that had spread extensively. Such graves are known, for example, from many places in France, Germany, Czechoslovakia, the Crimea, Palestine, North and East Africa, to Capetown in South Africa.

It is clear that such burial techniques point to the fact that the Neanderthalers and the men of the ice age were convinced that death was not the end of the matter.

Interesting about this is the view of the German investigator Kuhn. He thinks that this complex of practices teaches us that these men had no conception of the existence of a "soul." When man died no soul was liberated that lived on in a "Jenseits," but man stayed on this earth, be it at another place and invisible. He remained here and thus was in need of weapons, ornaments and food. With stones he had to be protected, with ash he had to be warmed, ocher had to give him a livelier color. To prevent the departed from returning he was bound tightly, knees flexed. The dead one is thus, according to Kuhn, a "lebender Leichnam" (a living corpse) which stays in the "Diesseits" (on this side of the grave).[46]

In this presentation the world is one entity. An abstract soul, an abstract heaven does not exist. "This world is a living in immanency, bound by directing the view at reality, the actual. The unreal is strange to him, strange to him is the beyond and the abstract. Man has an intimate union with nature, he has a definite task in the world that surrounds him. . . . Thinking has a fixed point with reference to which all life and work is fashioned, and this fixed point is the concrete reality."[47]

The second point, the *cultus* (worship), takes us to the meaning of the art of the last ice age. Investigators today are pretty well unanimous that this art had a definite religious sense, with the emphasis upon the magic, the bewitchment. For this, among others, the following arguments are adduced. When a human being was represented, then this occurred in the form of the image of a woman which supposedly symbolizes fertility, or in the form of a sorcerer or masked dancer.

Hardly ever is the face represented, this having some connection with dangers that were related thereto, even among many recent peoples. Next to these portraitures of human beings, which are fairly scarce, there were found thousands of pictures of animals: mammoths, bison, bears, horses and the like. Strikingly, figures of plants are wanting.

These representations of animals are viewed in the sense that they were made in order to represent the animal as under the dominance of the charm of man. Evidence for this view is that figures of animals have been found that were shot at and that were mutilated. We should interpret this art in the same way as the habit of the witches in the Middle Ages, who made dolls of people they wished to kill. They would cut off the head of the doll or stab it through with needles.

There are thus various arguments which support the opinion that the caves in which these pictures were found were consecrated places, where the sorcerers executed their magic cults.

---

[46] H. Kühn, 1954, *op cit.*, p. 149ff.: See also the opinion of H. Breuil, "Die ältere und mittlere Altsteinzeit," *Historia Mundi I*, pp. 259-288, 1952.
[47] H. Kühn, 1954, *op. cit.*, p. 159.

In the same way we can interpret the engraved stones that have been found in France which were thrown into the river in such a fashion that the images were face down. The portrayed animals were killed magically.

Finally, it is thought that a few portraitures of sorcerer's ceremonies have been found.

Naturally, one may differ in opinion as to just to what extent this witchcraft should be considered religious, or that it is only a primitive way to outwit wild life. However, it has been definitely determined that the findings point out that man of the ice age thought he could exercise magical power over the animals.

The last point which we shall touch upon is that of the *idea of God*. It is thought concerning this point that a few things can be deduced from some interesting findings.

The most important of these was made in August, 1920, in Eastern Switzerland, in "Drachenloch" which is situated at a height of 2445 m.[48] In this highly situated cave there was found in a stratum which dates back to the early Neanderthal times (Mousterian) of the Third Interglacial Period, among others a chest built of piled-up stones, which was closed with a cover (see Fig. 18). When this chest was opened there were found seven entire skulls and a few long bones of cave-bears neatly piled on top of one another. Further, there were in this cave noteworthy piles of bones.

All kinds of speculations have been made about the significance of the remarkable contents of this oldest known human structure, dating back perhaps 150,000 years.

It has been suggested that we have here a storage place for food, but the number of skulls is too few to make this have sense. It has also been proposed that the skulls were preserved because of the brains as these are a good material for tanning. But later it was concluded that the value of brains for tanning was discovered only after the last ice age.

Today there are two opposite interpretations. The first is of the Swiss Meuli. He thinks that we are dealing here with ritual

---

[48] H. Bächler, *Die ersten Bewohner der Schweiz*, Bern, 1947.

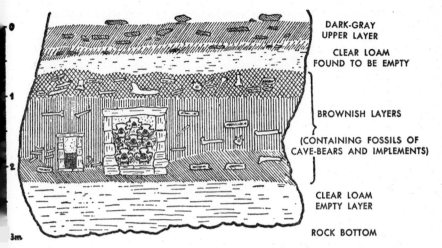

DARK-GRAY
UPPER LAYER

CLEAR LOAM
FOUND TO BE EMPTY

BROWNISH LAYERS

(CONTAINING FOSSILS OF
CAVE-BEARS AND IMPLEMENTS)

CLEAR LOAM
EMPTY LAYER

ROCK BOTTOM

Fig 18. Profile of the bottom of the "Drachenloch" in Eastern Switzerland. (From: H. Bächler, *Die ersten Bewohner der Schweiz*, 1947.)

burials of animals. He bases his opinion upon the observation that with some recent primitive peoples the hunter and the herdsman feel that they are very closely associated with the animals. The belief is widespread that man and the animal originally lived in peace with one another. After that man began to kill the animal and, to retain good relations notwithstanding, man performs definite actions. The debt of killing the animal is supposed to be atoned in this fashion. That is why a few parts of the skeleton of the animal, which are viewed as still being the animal, are deposited at a definite place. The idea of these actions is to give back to the animal that which he needs to return to life. From a few bones—a rib, the skull, the long bones—the animal can again be reconstructed. This secures the favorable development of the future hunt. The hunter has atoned for his debt and the animal is satisfied.[49]

Over against this opinion there is a second which views the findings of these bear skulls as sacrifices. This opinion was held first by the German Schmidt,[50] but now also, among others,

---

[49] See Bächler, *op. cit.*, 1947, p. 149.

[50] E.g., P. W. Schmidt, "Die Urkulturen," *Historia Mundi I*, Bern, pp. 375–501, 1952.

by Koppers[51] and Kühn.[52]   They also arrived at this hypothesis upon the basis of ethnological observations. It has been discovered that the same custom of arranging skulls and long bones of bears and reindeer still occurs today among the Eskimo tribes in Arctic America. Here it appears to be a sacrifice to the divinity, in particular a sacrifice of the firstlings of the chase, the "Primitialopfer." It is unusually interesting that not only analogous animal sacrifices, but also botanical first-fruits offerings are currently observed among widely separated primitive peoples. They are found, for example, among the Indians of California, and also among the Pygmy tribes of Africa. The wide distribution of this custom, according to the investigators named, points to the fact that it goes back traditionally to very ancient times, so that even the findings in Switzerland can be thus explained.   It is thought that we can go even a step farther.   The ethnological research of recent date has brought to light, according to them, that not only the peoples already named, but that also, for example, some old tribes on the Fuegian Islands and in India are monotheistic.   These nations believe in only one God who created the world and who gives them their daily food. Thus these investigators come to the conclusion that the first religion of man was "primitive monotheism" (Urmonotheismus), and that all other forms of religion (animism, polytheism, etc.) arose secondarily. Thus, according to this idea, the Neanderthalers could have been monotheists.

Viewed in this light the "Primitialopfer" contains a beautiful idea.   Because then the offering is not given as food for the Deity, who of course possesses everything, and thus has no need of it, but as a symbol of gratitude, dependence and prayer.   Schmidt expresses it as follows: "This acknowledgement of the highest ownership is the first sense and purpose of the 'Primitalopfer,' and with that it becomes an offer of praise and adoration; accompanying brief prayers also often speak expressly of this sense.   To the prayer of adoration and praise is easily added gratitude for the good providence of God, similarly often expressed in accompanying prayers, so that therewith the primitive offering becomes also a thanksoffering."[53]

51 W. Koppers, *Der Urmensch und sein Weltbild*, Wien, 1949.
52 H. Kühn, *op. cit.*, 1954, p. 166ff.
53 P. W. Schmidt, *op. cit.*, 1952, p. 494.

With the mentioning of a similar ancient bear ritual, found not only in the Upper Pleistocene Epoch of Switzerland, but also in Germany and Austria, we conclude our discussion of this form of sacrifices.

In this connection the question is very important whether there are any data from which we can deduce something about the place where it was thought the god or the divinity lived. We follow here the reasoning of the German Rust. He is of the opinion that, seeing all the old religions think of the realm of the dead and the eternal hunting grounds as "earthbound," we may expect the same thing of the men of the ice age.[54] He thinks it probable that they considered the divinity as living in the underworld. As arguments he adduces that the cave paintings were made deep down in the caves, thus at the entrances to the lower world, but he points particularly to the interesting sacrifical place found by himself near Ahrensburg in the vicinity of Hamburg. There he found in layers of peat, originating from a pool dating from the last ice age, entire skeletons of reindeer that had one large stone or several smaller stones, sometimes weighing 8-10 kg., in the chest. These reindeer were shot in the open country and thus not bred. This is evident from the riddled shoulder-blades and the wooden arrows that lay in the chest. In all there were found thirty such skeletons. Hence, here are thirty reindeer drowned in a pool. Research has shown that here only female animals of two years were concerned. Further, there were 30,000 bones, horns, implements, weapons and works of art in the pool. From all this Rust is convinced that we have here an important sacrificial place. There was found in addition a pole 2.5 m. long and 12 cm. thick which must have stood in the water at the edge. Upon this pole there was found the skull of a reindeer. Also this was peculiar. It was the skull of the oldest animal present among the thousand reindeer found at this place. It came from a sixteen-year old reindeer cow. According to Rust, this points to the fact that the pole had not been placed here for profane reasons, but that there must have been a cultistic, religious reason. It should be added that if it had been the wish to place upon the pole a beautiful

---

[54] A. Rust, "Die jüngere Altsteinzeit," *Historia Mundi I*, Bern, pp. 289-317, 1952.

hunting trophy, a male skull would have been more appropriate. There were even found splendid antlers with a width of 1.5 m. The antlers of the reindeer cows are in themselves already less developed than those of the bulls, but after ten years they even become reduced.

From all this we truly get the impression that we must ascribe to this pool religious significance as a sacrifical place. Rust considers it very well possible that sacrifices were brought into this pool so that in this way they could reach the underworld. He points out that in fairy tales about bottomless seas and springs we perhaps find an echo of this idea.

If in the mountainous territories the caves were the entrances to the underworld, on level land it was the pools and the like that served this purpose.

From the little that has been told here about the sacrifices of the Neanderthalers and the men of the ice age, it may appear that there are important arguments in favor of the view that these people already believed in God, or gods, that controlled life upon this earth. If by further research this is confirmed, then there is all the more reason to view these people in every respect as entirely worthy of being considered human.

5. *Genesis and Prehistory*

A very important question for us is that concerning the relation between the results of historic-anthropologic research and the communications in the first chapters of Genesis.

On the one hand, as we mentioned in the first chapter of this book, we meet with the opinion that they have nothing to do with each other, since Genesis concerns itself only with the divine message of creation, fall and salvation, cast in a mold which has no factually real significance, so that it is senseless to confront the scientific results with the Bible.

On the other hand we meet with the fundamentalistic idea that the text of Genesis, besides the message of salvation, very definitely gives historically and scientifically exact knowledge, so that the believer in scriptural science is not only compelled to confront the Bible and science with each other, but that even the truth of scientific data must be measured by the literal communications of the Bible.

As we explained before, it seems to us that both lines of thought do injustice to Scripture. The first, because it separates the reality of the history of origin and of salvation from the reality in which this was enacted when we view the concrete character of the biblical communications. The second opinion does injury to Scripture because it lapses into the error of supposing that Genesis has been written in our scientifically defined concepts.

Therefore, it seems plausible to state that Genesis imparts to us the main motives for the existence of this world and of the life of man in concrete form, in which this concretism is really essential. But then we must view it in such a way that we may not consider the language of the Bible as scientifically conceptual language; hence, we may never demand from Scripture exact physical, astronomical, biological and thus also not exact historical knowledge.

In order to develop and to demarcate this point of view, we shall offer in the following pages four speculative correlations, almost in experimental fashion (see Fig. 19).

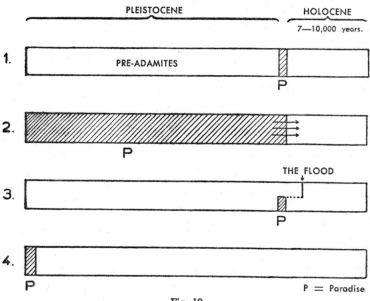

Fig. 19.

a. With the first attempt at correlation we proceed for once (fundamentalistically) from the point of view that the genealogies of Genesis deserve to have ascribed to them real historical value. The age of the human race is then 6,000 to 7,000 years. Eventually the genealogies were schematized so that an age of 10,000 years is not considered impossible.

This means that mankind originated only after the last ice age. We then arrive at the difficulty of how to regard the Neanderthalers and the men of the ice age, not to mention the manufacturers of implements from the beginning of the Pleistocene Epoch. When we persist in considering these as human beings, then the only solution is that they were so-called "pre-Adamites" who all died out when Adam became the progenitor of the whole recent human race. This reasoning is understandable, logical and conclusive. Yet there are different arguments to be adduced why this does not satisfy. In the first place, there are various recent tribes with some anatomical features that as such are not inherent in *Homo sapiens*, but go back to older forms. Thus the skull of the Australian natives possesses features that sooner can be called neanderthaloid or even pithecanthropoid. Further, in the case of various tribes it is probable that they have lived very much longer in their present isolated biotype than 10,000 years. This is true, for example, of the Pygmies and the Bushmen, but also of the Eskimos, who most likely followed the receding land-ice and the related Arctic fauna, and as, among others, is also evident from Scandinavian mountain-wall art.[55] Of greater importance, however, is the objection that this reasoning on the one hand rescues the genealogies of Genesis by ascribing to them exact scientific significance, but, on the other hand, abandons the idea that Adam was absolutely the very first man. The one is relinquished at the expense of the other.

One may try to overcome this difficulty by stating that only the Adam of about 10,000 years ago was a complete man, while there was still lacking in the pre-Adamites one thing and another. But this idea appears improbable in the light of our knowledge of the cultures of the Neanderthalers and men of the ice age, of which we gave a summary review in the preceding pages.

---

[55] See J. Maringer and H. G. Bandi, *op. cit.*, 1953.

b. According to a second possibility, which is conceivable and can be found in part in literature, the long series of human-like beings from the Pleistocene Epoch should not be placed previous to paradise, but in it.[56] This signifies that the whole of the Pleistocene is viewed as the time of paradise, after which recent man arose. Also in this line of thought the duration of the genealogies can be historically correct.

One can correlate even more profoundly this line of thought with the story of paradise by accepting that Pleistocene man lived in a "state of rectitude" to this extent that he did not know the concepts of "good" and "evil"; that he did not know either that man has a "spirit"; that he did not know anything at all about an hereafter and thus also did not view his dead as corpses but rigid living beings who had to be supplied food, weapons and the like, and who had to be tied to prevent them from returning. At the same time it was known that God existed, but it was thought that he lived here upon the earth, underground. That is the explanation of the concrete (not burned up) sacrifice of skulls of bears, reindeer, etc. One can point out that the men of the ice age drew only pictures of animals and human beings, but never of plants. One can correlate this with the commission which man received from God (see Genesis 2:19-20) to name the animals, while the plants are not mentioned which seems strange for our modern sentiment.

Through one cause or another, the fall of man, the distinction between good and evil, has been discovered. Man has learned that he has a "soul," that there is an hereafter and a heaven where God dwells. On account of this the distance between God and man becomes so great that it hardly could be bridged. One had to call upon the Lord (Gen. 4:26). That is why the burnt offering arose with ascending smoke. Thence originated conflict and doubt in the heart of man. To die meant death. That is why man had to work to obtain his bread, agriculture arose, etc.

This reasoning undoubtedly has some attractive aspects. A preponderant objection, however, is that from the story of paradise in Genesis and the general religious significance which is attached to it elsewhere in Scripture (cf., *e.g.*, Acts 17:26; Romans 5), we

---

[56] See, e.g., H. Kühn, *op. cit.*, 1954, p. 159.

get the strong impression that it is considered essential that only two people lived in the Garden of Eden.

c. Theoretically a third line of thought can be proposed which combines more or less a few main features of both preceding hypotheses. From the first hypothesis we take over that Adam and Eve were indeed the progenitors of all recent men and thus lived about 10,000 years ago. Of the second hypothesis we accept that besides these two, and before them, there lived a widespread population of entirely similar men. Only these two people lived, however, in the Garden of Eden; only these two acquired the knowledge of good and evil; only these two are the common ancestors of all recent men. When they left the Garden, they thus did not come into an entirely uninhabited world.

This line of argument "explains" why Cain, after the death of his brother Abel, was afraid that everyone he would meet in his wanderings would kill him, while according to the current opinion only Adam and Eve, his father and his mother, were left over. This reasoning also "explains" why Cain could marry and what it meant that the sons of God took themselves wives from the daughters of men (Genesis 6:2). According to this hypothesis one could propose that the line of Adam and Eve became the genealogical line of all recent mankind only when through the Flood (or, among others, through the Flood) all other human lines were cut off. This hypothesis also makes somewhat clearer the difference between Genesis 1, where God made *men* and Genesis 2, where God placed *the* man in the Garden of Eden.

The extensive distribution of man already during the Pleistocene Epoch, the advanced culture during the Last Glacial Period and especially cannibalism and similar customs before Adam, however, constitute just as many important objections against this hypothesis.

d. Therefore, let us finally advance a fourth possibility, whereby the *historical* historicity of the genealogies, over which all previous hypotheses stumble, is denied, but whereby the unity, the monophylogeny, of the human race, is the prime consideration. Starting from the idea that all beings that manufacture implements (or/and use fire), must be viewed as human beings, we should conclude that man lived already during the entire Pleistocene Epoch, hence, according to our present knowledge, for at least half a million years.

The question when paradise existed is not only answered by the foregoing, but also by the observation of the cannibalism and the killing of congeners during the entire Pleistocene Epoch.

The first man and paradise are thus limited at the latest to the beginning of the Pleistocene. This means that the first human being could have been of the *sapiens* type, if the old *sapiens* specimens by further research indeed prove to be that old, or that the first man morphologically had more features in common with the anthropoids than we have.

By placing the first man at the beginning of the Pleistocene Epoch, various data of Genesis are "explained." The text makes it probably (nothing more!) that only after paradise animals were killed: the skins which man received as clothing, the sacrifice of Abel and the like. Also the fact that all known human-like forms from the Pleistocene Epoch were pronouncedly carnivorous argues for an early paradise.

In paradise man was recognizably not pronouncedly carnivorous or omniverous, but more fructivorous. Now, the remarkable thing is that of late voices are heard of those who think that indeed the oldest human-like forms, particularly the giants, must be viewed as fructivorous, especially upon the basis of the consideration that the eating of plantlike food requires massive jaws and teeth and strong muscles of mastication.[57] When, in addition we think of the fact that the other higher Primates, namely the anthropoids, are mainly fructivorous, then this view receives a definite emphasis. Besides, the fructivorous forms are ever bound locally to a wooded biotype. The transition from the predominant fructivorous paradisian condition to the omnivorous post-paradisian condition, has thus also an important biological significance. Of course, only this omnivorous or carnivorous man can leave the wooded biotype, since he finds food everywhere and, besides, can pursue wildlife. One can speculate even farther and from the changed choice of food he can expect some influence upon the skull. To eat flesh requires less massive molars than when one eats plants, and thus also requires a smaller jaw and less developed muscles of mastica-

---

[57] *E.g.,* J. T. Robinson, *Evolution*, 8, pp. 324-334, 1954.

tion, so that the pressure on the calvarium, where the masticatory muscles are attached, becomes less and the brain cavity can become larger. This fourth possibility that has been touched upon thus also implies that we should not exclude the idea that the first human being looked much more anthropoid-like than we do and, at the same time, that the shape of the human skeleton, particularly the skull, is much more variable than we had thought for a long time. The text of Genesis 6 tells that "in those days . . . of old" (vs. 4) there lived Nephilim—giants. This does not then surprise us. It is not impossible that Adam and Eve were giants.

We wish to add a few supplements. The sacrifice brought by Abel, "of the firstlings of his flock," makes us think of the "Primitialopfer" of the Neanderthalers. The preference which the men of the ice age gave to the portraiture of animals can be viewed in the light of Genesis, which clearly gives preference to the animals above the plants. We referred already to the giving of names. The vegetable sacrifice of Cain was not accepted. We also should think of the fact that throughout the entire Pleistocene Epoch implements were already manufactured and that Genesis places this custom, significantly, after the story of paradise.

Against this fourth hypothesis it may be argued, among others, that it is not only hampered by the genealogies but also by the sequence of the communications in Genesis 2 through 6, where, for example, Jubal, the flutist, is mentioned early and the giants much later, while the data of science inclines us to reverse this order.

Although both sources, by accurate reading and reflection, give us more room for discussion than appears at first (that flutes are known only from the last ice age does not mean necessarily that there were no musical instruments before; Genesis 6:4 points out that the giants already existed earlier), yet this objection touches upon an essential point which, in considering the first chapters of Genesis, will have to be reviewed. Namely, if it is correct that these chapters give us fragments dating from a long period of time (the Pleistocene Epoch), then we should consider the following possibility: the writer of Scripture did not know anything about the age of the earth and of living creatures being millions of years old, just as little as he knew that many stars are millions of light years away from us. When he viewed the stars he adjusted these with the sun and the moon, as it were, on one level, "the firmament," which was situated at a relatively short distance from the earth. Analogically to this one can try to realize that, when the writer of Scripture saw the fragments of happenings of the hoary past, which, under divine guidance had been saved, through lack of knowledge and imagination he, as it were, contracted these to a level dating of only a few thousand years ago.

Just as in the "firmament" *before* and *after* are lost, so on this level *sooner* and *later* lost sense. The fact that the writers of the Bible did not purpose at all to give a historical account, we see particularly in Genesis 2 where the sequence of creation is exactly the opposite as in Genesis 1.

In this proposition nothing is detracted from the historicity of the biblical statements, (Enoch, Jubal, Noah, are fully recognized as persons), but it is no scientific-*historical* historicity. Consequently the genealogies similarly have not the same historical correctness, as, *e.g.*, the family tree of the Royal House of the Netherlands, as it is found in the history books.

We should realize that, if Genesis is not a scientific or biological book, it also has not been written to impart to us the *science* of history. It is not a technical history book.

In the preceding we have reviewed four strongly speculative and debatable possibilities about the relation between the results of scientific research and the first chapters of Genesis. Our aim in this connection is not to argue in detail about our own *present* preference for the fourth hypothesis. We state also emphatically that the possibility is not suggested that such an attempt ever will have the chance to succeed.

We can never "reconcile" revelation with the reality of nature, (a much-used expression), or clamp them down; but we are able to experience that they constitute one transaction. That is why sometimes we can see more clearly the meaning of scientific data in the light of the Bible. For that reason, similarly, we sometimes can understand Bible texts better through our scientific knowledge.

In that sense the four speculative-experimental hypotheses may have demonstrated that there are so many points of resemblance between pre-history and the "in those days . . . of old" of Genesis, thus described and designated, that it deserves serious consideration whether we should not try to see the wording of this part of the Bible in a different sense than has been customary up till now in our circles. The preference of the animals above the plants, the frugivory in paradise and the carnivory after that, the concrete terrestrial presence of God who walks and talks with man, the "Primitialopfer" of the firstlings of Abel's herd, the possible biological sign on Cain, the beginning of culture with Jubal and his brothers, the giants—and yet various other factors—seem to make it worthy of consideration to turn our thoughts in that direction.

6. *Creationism and the Problem of the Origin of Man*

Before we go deeper into this question, it will be well to summarize briefly the most important points of the preceding.

a. In the first place, it appears that the investigation of the skeletal remnants of the oldest human-like beings known do not give us an answer to the question where and how man originated.

b. Next, we think that upon the basis of our present available data we must conclude that man has been present upon the earth at least since the beginning of the Pleistocene Epoch.

c. It is a subject for consideration whether the first chapters of Genesis have reference to the history of this Pleistocene man.

When upon the basis of a. and b. we ask ourselves how man originated, then we see that the investigation concerning this has not given us what had been expected half a century ago. The descent from one of the recent anthropoids is generally unanimously rejected. Because of the lack of any indication from the period before the Pleistocene Epoch, at present all that meets the eye in the literature about the origin of man is pure speculation.

Next we shall discuss the problem whether for us as Christians the *possibility* of a genetic connection between man and animal has to be cut short in advance. In the approach to this problem it is necessary for us to reflect upon the resemblances and the differences between man and the recent anthropoids.

That man, viewed superficially, has a pronounced resemblance to these animals, is plain to everyone. A few examples will make it clear that this resemblance is more than superficial.

When man is born he has a maxilla (upper jaw) which consists of only one bone. In this respect he differs fairly well from all other mammals since with them the maxilla at birth, and often during their entire life, is constructed of four bones of which the anterior two carry the incisors and the posterior two the canines and the premolars and molars. With the gorilla and the orangutan at birth we also find these four bones, which only fuse at maturity. The chimpanzee among all mammals is the only animal that has exactly the same maxillary relations as man (see Fig. 20).

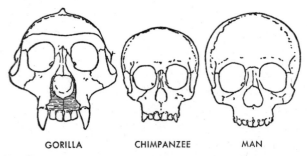

GORILLA   CHIMPANZEE   MAN

Fig. 20. The gorilla often retains till maturity the separation between the four bones of the upper jaw. Only with the chimpanzee and man are they already completely fused at birth. (From Weinert, *Stammesentwicklung der Menschheit*)

The second characteristic has reference to the carpus (wrist). Here we find in mammals only one little bone that can be designated by the name *central* (many other vertebrates have four). We find this condition with all apes and also with the gibbons and the orangutans. With man, however, the peculiarity presents itself that this central body is initially formed as a separate bone, but that it soon splits into two pieces, each one fusing with another carpal bone. The same condition is found only with the gorilla and the chimpanzee.

A third feature has reference to the chest. With all monkeys the chest is about as broad as it is deep. Only in the case of the anthropoids and man is the chest much broader than it is deep, which gives an entirely different impression.[58]

As a corollary to this it can be pointed out that the sternum of the anthropoids and man is much broader than with the monkeys and, besides, that with the latter it is built up from a whole series of small bones. while with the former, although in origin the condition is the same there is a tendency to fusion of these separate bones. With some old anthropoids and with all humans this results in a sternum composed of one piece.

In addition, a great number of characters could be named from which it is evident that man, morphologically speaking, shows a very close relation to the anthropoids.

Incidentally it may be mentioned that upon the basis of these anatomical correspondences attempts have been made for a long time to find out to which of the four anthropoids man is most closely related phylogenetically, from which one he descended or with which one he may have had the last common ancestor. As we mentioned earlier in the discussion of the origin of the vertebrates, it is not possible upon the basis of the anatomy of recent organisms to obtain *certain* data on phylogeny. This is the case also here because very divergent views have been presented. We saw already that Dubois (p. 145) later in life, upon the basis of anatomical characters, came to the conclusion that man descended from a gibbon. Opposed to this is the very strongly expressed opinion of Weinert, that man phylogenetically is most closely related to the chimpanzee, while other investigators propagate still other opinions.[59]

At present most investigators come to the conclusion that man does not descend from one definite recent anthropoid, that he is not related more closely with the one than with the other, but that they all long ago had common ancestors by which the corresponding characters may be explained.

But not only anatomically, also physiologically, man shows a very strong resemblance to the anthropoids. We select again some examples to illustrate this.

---

[58] See A. H. Schultz, *Cold Spring Harbor Symp. on Quant. Biol.*, 15, pp. 40-41, 1950.

[59] H. Weinert, *op. cit.*, 1944 and 1951.

When we inject a rabbit with a small amount of blood of another species of animals, for example, of a horse, then there are formed in the blood serum substances that react specifically to the foreign blood. If after some time some blood is withdrawn from the rabbit and added to the serum of the horse, a precipitate is formed. A precipitate does not occur when the serum of a cow is added to the serum of this rabbit because no specific antibodies are present against this. In this way, it is thought, it can be traced whether two species of animals are related, because in that case a more or less clear reaction will appear. For example, if a rabbit has first been injected with the blood of a dog, then it appears later that it will react not only to serum of dogs but also of wolves. Or, if we pretreat a rabbit with blood of a horse, then its serum reacts later also to the serum of asses.

It is a question of great importance to know what the precipitate is when the serum of a rabbit, which has been sensitized to human blood, is added to the serum of other Primates. Among others, this experiment has been carried out by the German investigator Mollison.[60] The result of this was that with the serum of Prosimians no reaction or hardly any reaction, took place; with that of the American monkeys (Platyrrhina) little; with the Old World monkeys (Cercopithecidae) a definite reaction. The serum of the orangutan gave a reaction hardly any stronger than that of the Cercopithecidae. Serum of the chimpanzee, however, reacted almost just as strongly as human serum.

The explanation which has been given for this is as follows. This reaction depends upon the presence of definite proteins in the blood serum. The shorter the time has been since two animals had a common ancestor, the more correspondences the proteins show and the stronger the reaction is in "serological" experiments of this kind.

Also the investigation of the blood groups has brought to light many similarities. As is known, every human being belongs to one of the following groups: A, B, AB, or O. It has become evident that the same types of blood occur in the anthropoids. Gibbons,

---

[60] See for these statements about the blood H. Weinert, *op. cit.*, 1944, p. 94ff; P. Kramp, "Zur Abstammung des Menschen," in *Schöpfungsglaube und Evolutionstheorie*, 1955, p. 84ff.; E. A. Hooton, *op. cit.*, 1946, p. 44ff.

orangutans and gorillas have the types A, B and AB, but not O; chimpanzees A and O, but not B and AB.

When we review the above data then the most prudent conclusion that we can draw is that, upon the basis of anatomical and physiological research, it is evident that man and the recent anthropoids have a great number of characters in common.

The investigator Bijlmer, after an exposition of these similarities, arrives at the conclusion: "Man zoologically shows himself to be equally closely related to the chimpanzee as a sheep to a goat. It is not known to me what mental gymnastics the opponents of the doctrine of descent comfort themselves with to escape the consequence of this simple fact. And why all the difficulty?"[61]

As inborn opponent of the dogmatical doctrine of descent we cannot suppress the inclination to demonstrate to this author (who apparently has given himself a higher mark in spiritual exercise than his opponents on whose skill he casts doubt, without knowing them) and others to what extent and why we think that the relation between man and chimpanzee is not such a simple fact as that between sheep and goat.

There is first of all the zoological method of Weidenreich. With him we find the following expression, which should be taken to heart: "But if we want to know the course taken by human evolution, we have to take into account not the congruities between the organization of man and the great apes, but their most characteristic differences."[62]

And then follow the criteria which we rendered in the second section of this chapter (p. 153). When we apply these we come to the conclusion that man did not descend directly from one of the recent anthropoids. As we saw, this does not give a solution to the problem of the Australopithecinae because here the criteria fail. "If the morphological criteria which I consider as decisive for the distinction of man and anthropoids are applied to these Australopithecus types, the diagnosis is not easy, for the latter combine human characters with simian ones in a way which has never been observed before."[63]

---

[61] H. J. T. Bijlmer, *De evolutie van de mens*, The Hague, 1946, p. 89.
[62] Weidenreich, *Apes, etc.*, 1948, p. 5.
[63] Weidenreich, *Apes, etc.*, 1948, p. 20.

This means, accordingly, that in the past there have lived animals that resembled man even much more than the present anthropoids, so much in fact that upon the basis of the skeletal remnants which have been found, it is not possible to say whether they were animals or humans.

In consideration of *only these* data the conclusion is apparent that man is "zoologically" (Bijlmer) very closely related to the anthropoid group in general, which relation implies a common descent.

However, we have seen earlier that Weidenreich, nevertheless, sees characteristic differences which should be taken into consideration in connection with the problem of descent and of which the reflection is found in the "cultural objects." By giving room for these views he has already left the realm of the purely zoological.

During recent years other data have been advanced which indicate that the problem, even viewed zoologically, is not as simple as had been thought for a long time. Hence a new look is beginning to develop in regard to this problem. Especially the Swiss Portmann has argued for this movement.[64] He directs his attention thereby especially upon the embryological development and the first year of the life of man during which periods he is being prepared for life. The helpless babe in the cradle makes us think very strongly about the corresponding stadia in birds and mammals, where also often the young for some time lie in the nest entirely dependent upon the parents.

When we review a little more accurately the first period of the existence of birds and mammals, we at once notice two types which can be illustrated by pointing on the one hand to the dogs and cats that are born blind and, on the other hand, to the lively colts and calves that are ready for all kinds of activity. How is this difference distributed among the mammals?

It appears that the mammals that have a little specialized bodily structure, and possess relatively slightly developed brains, usually have a short gravidity. They have a great number of offspring which show a helpless condition immediately after birth. These

---

[64] A. Portmann, *Vom Ursprung des Menschen*, Basle, 1944; *Von der Idee des Humanen in der Gegenwärtigen Biologie*, St. Gallen, 1951; *Biologische Fragmente zu einer Lehre vom Menschen*, Basle, 1951.

young have little or no hair, their ears and eyes are still closed and their body temperature is dependent upon the environment. This condition is found among the Insectivora, among many rodents and the small carnivores. These animals are said to be "nidicolous" (nest-dwellers). With the mammals that are more highly specialized, such as the hoofed animals, seals, whales, Prosimians and monkeys, the development within the mother lasts much longer, the number of young is mostly one or two, and these are far advanced in development. They resemble their parents already to a large extent. They know how to use their sense-organs and muscles entirely in the correct fashion. They are "nidifugous" (nest-fleers).

The difference is conspicuous when we look at young squirrels, in whom the eyes open only after a month, and compare them with colts that at once follow the herd.

We saw a moment ago that the eyes, ears and nostrils were open at birth with these nidifugous animals. During the embryological development, however, these animals also go through a period in which these sense organs are closed. This condition thus continues with the nidicolous animals after birth. The nidifugous animals are born only after this period.

How is this condition with the recent anthropoids and man? Are these nidicolous or nidifugous?

With man gravidity is about 266 days; with the chimpanzee 237 days, with the orangutan 275 days. As far as the gorilla is concerned, exact data are lacking. The lower apes have a much shorter gravid period. Thus, for example, the rhesus monkey 167 days. With all anthropoids and man the number of young is small. On the basis of these characters one also would be inclined to think that anthropoids and man resemble each other. By more accurate observation this does not appear to be the case.

All young anthropoids are nidifugous. They are born with

---

* Translator's Note: The terms "nest-remainers" and "nest-fleers" are not elegant English words and it is questionable whether their use is permissible. *Nidicolous* and *nidifugous* are exact translations of these terms. Even though their use is not common, yet they are heard in scientific circles. *Altricial* and *precocial* are synonomous terms that are used more frequently and are confined to ornithology.

open eyes and, further, with well-developed sense organs. Besides, they are able to perform all kinds of actions. They do not lie helpless in a nest for a period of time. The most striking thing is that the young stubbornly hold on to the hairy skin of the mother with their four hands, by which action they are safe during the journey through the primeval forest. After a month the young chimpanzee occasionally will sit on the ground. After six weeks it can stand upright, holding on to its mother. From all these data we must conclude that the young anthropoids are pronouncedly nidifugous.

Man, when he is born, lies for a long time helplessly in the cradle. At first view he thus seems nidicolous. But that is not true in every respect. The most obvious difference is that his sense organs can already be used. Man also passes through a period in which the eyelids, the auditory canals and the nostrils are closed, namely, from the third to the fifth month of pregnancy.

This means, and that is an interesting statement, that if man were really nidicolous just as dogs and cats, he would have to be born at about the fourth month.

In reality man continues to grow for another five months in the mother animal and thus follows the nidifugous type, as all higher mammals. But in spite of that difference he still stays in the "nest." This is thus a pronounced typical difference between anthropoids and man. Man begins as a nidifugous-nidicolous creature; he starts as an "infant" and not as a "young" animal.

But also when we compare the proportions of the young of the anthropoids and the human infant, we at once notice a distinct difference. With the higher mammals the young resemble very much the mature animals. A young roe or the young of a whale are exactly small editions of the parents, except that in some cases the head of the young is proportionately a little larger. However, an infant in many of its measurements, is differently proportioned than its parents. Also as far as the measurements of the body are concerned the infant just born displays an entirely peculiar type among the Primates.

The study of the weight of body shows the same. The helpless-ness of the infant compared with the activity of the young anthropoids would make us suspect that the birthweight of man would be lower than that of the anthropoids, particularly than that of the gorilla which is 2.5 to 3 times as heavy as a full-grown human being. This expectation is put to shame because an infant just born on the average weighs much more than the young of anthropoids (Fig. 21).

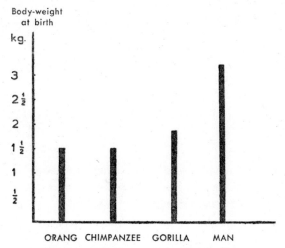

Fig. 21. Comparative body-weight at birth.

This enigmatic deviation of man becomes somewhat comprehensible when we view the proportional weight of the most central organ of the higher animals, namely, the brain. Then at the same time, also the other details that were discussed will be placed in a special light.

With various nidicolous animals it was stated that the weight of the brain of the mature animal was 4.7 to 8.9 times that of the weight at birth, with many nidifugous ones 2.0 to 3.6, and with man 3.6 to 3.9. With the nidicolous animals the brain at the time of birth thus is relatively small, with the nidifugous relatively larger. We notice that man, in regard to this character, belongs more to the nidifugous than to the nidicolous.

It can thus be stated that there is a certain agreement in proportion between the weight of the brain of young and mature individuals of anthropoids and man. However, the case becomes different when we view the absolute weight of the brain, because then it appears that the anthropoids at birth have a weight of the brain of about 130 grams and man about 370 grams, while in full-grown anthropoids and man the figures are respectively 400 and 1350 grams.

From this statement it becomes clear to us why our infants are so heavy. They are born with a weight of the brain nearly three times as great as that of the anthropoids. This cannot be accomplished except in a body that is also much heavier.

We have established in the preceding that man is not truly nidicolous, because then the length of gravidity would be only four months. We shall now be made to realize that man is also not truly nidifugous.

If man normally was nidifugous then he should have at birth the same proportions as those of an adult; however, he also should be able to assume the specifically orthograde position and should be able to walk. In addition, he should have at his disposal the first rudiments of communication, of speech by word and gesture. When we examine at what time man reaches this stage we come to the conclusion that this occurs about one year after birth. Hence, after one year man has reached the stage of development which a truly nidifugous creature has attained already at birth.

This means that if the condition of man was such as a zoologist has a right to expect of a nidifugous creature, pregnancy should not last nine months but twenty-one. Such long periods of gravidity do occur. With the sperm-whale, for instance, pregnancy lasts 16 months while its young at birth is 4 meters long. The Indian elephant has a pregnancy of 21 to 22 months and the young animal, weighing 100 kilograms at birth, is able to walk at once. The birth of man is thus, viewed from a zoological point of view, a premature birth.

The peculiarity of the condition of man we can picture best by reviewing the different types of births of quadruped vertebrates in the order of the stage in their development (cf. Fig. 22). We find the simplest condition with most of the reptiles. The young turtles, lizards, snakes and crocodiles generally crawl out of the eggs entirely ready for life. They are prepared immediately to undertake all kinds of activities. For the most part they do not even see their progenitors.

With the least developed birds a similar situation prevails. Chicks and ducklings can help themselves for the greater part. They are truly nidifugous.

The most highly developed birds, such as thrushes, gulls, woodpeckers and parrots, are nidicolous. The parent birds for some time fulfill the functions to make the further development of the young possible.

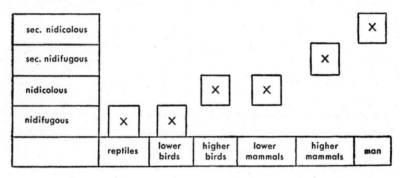

Fig. 22. Summary of nidicolous and nidifugous habits among reptiles, birds and mammals.

The same type of nidicolous condition we find with the lowly developed mammals, as we saw.

With the higher mammals, for instance, also the anthropoids, this nidicolous state is not sufficient to reach the higher stage of development. Here the problem is solved by retaining the young longer inside the body than with the nidicolous; even for such a long time that a new form of nidifugosity originates, which Portmann calls *"secondary nidifugosity."*

For the development of man even this is not sufficient. In man's case, to a long period of pregnancy is added an even longer period of helplessness. This entirely unique condition in the case of man Portmann designates with the term *"secondary nidicolosity."*

Man is thus the only secondarily nidicolous creature we know and displays therefore in his development an entirely peculiar, unique biological type.

This entirely unique type of development is of great importance.

The anthropoid is brought into this world with his fairly well complete fixed behavior and has to get along with what has been given to him. But man, speaking zoologically, is born prematurely. On account of this his development can unfold itself during one of the most sensitive periods in the full environment, in the family, and constantly in interchange with the full life of the parents, providers and, eventually, of brothers and sisters. That this is of great importance everyone understands who knows what great significance psychologists attach to the first year of one's life.

However, there are other biological differences that are to be mentioned; for example, when we watch the growth period. This seems to last longer with man than with any other mammal. Thus, for example, at birth the common whale is 7 meters long, after 6 months 14 meters, after 2 years 23 meters, while he reaches probably his maximal length of plus-minus 26 meters after 5 or 6 years. A lion is full grown after 6 to 7 years. An elephant takes 14 to 15 years for this.

The anthropoids complete their growth as follows: the gorilla after 7 years, the orangutan after 12 to 14 years, the chimpanzee after 11 to 12 years. Over against that we have man with 19 to 22 years.

Also the intensity of growth varies. With all mammals growth becomes slower and slower and the end of growth coincides about with the appearance of sexual maturity.

With man puberty is exactly one of the most intense growth periods; again here is a clear difference.

The last point of difference to which we wish to call attention is duration of life. It appears, namely, that the orangutan as well as the gorilla and the chimpanzee live only about 30 years. Hence man can live two or three times as long as the anthropoids. To this should be added that, in contrast with the animals, as man gets older it is often accompanied with a constantly greater development of that which is specifically human. The biotic becomes less potent, but the "spirit" often reaches in "gray old age" its greatest florescence and produces the most beautiful fruits. We see this in the case of many church fathers, scholars, artists, statemen. Here we also see a remarkable difference from all animals.

These data, gathered by Portmann, make it possible for us to illustrate why the problem of the origin of man is more difficult than that of the relation between "a sheep and a goat," why the relation between man and the anthropoids is not a "simple fact" and why the "consequence" of it is not so clear for the "opponents of the doctrine of descent."

In the first place, we should realize that the advocates of the *doctrine* of descent in their investigations usually, although sometimes unaware, sought especially after those characters in which man and the anthropoids agree. They were convinced in advance of this genetic relation. They knew already before they started with the investigation in which direction they wished to go, and through this they determined the insight into, the interpretation of and the terminology concerning the results that would be found. We noticed this, for instance, with the initial position of Dubois in connection with the *Pithecanthropus*, which position was determined entirely by Haeckel. The investigation served to prove a thesis. In this dogmatic attitude (*doctrine* of descent) one is soon inclined to consider the differences between man and the anthropoids as mere bagatelles. In a correct scientific reasoning, however, one should weigh carefully over against one another the arguments pro and con. Hence, we should keep in view not just the characteristics which man and the anthropoids have in common, but we should pay equally much attention to those in which they differ.

This leads us to the second remark. We should realize definitely that, thanks to evolutionism, our image of man has become entirely different. Before the year 1800 people were convinced that man is a being who differs essentially from the animals. His "bodily existence" shows a strong resemblance, but his "spiritual" attributes are entirely different. Man is *qualitatively* different. The entire image of man became different with the advent of the *doctrine* of descent, of evolutionism. Evolutionism holds, of course, that man *as a totality* is placed in the animal kingdom. This means that man not qualitatively, but *only quantitatively,* differs in characteristics from the animals. Or, as Haeckel expresses it pregnantly: "Just as the spiritual capacities of man were obtained step by step through the advancing adaptation of the brain and were established through lasting inheritance, so also the instincts of animals, which differ only quantitatively but not qualitatively from these, originated through the gradual evolution of the organ of their soul, the central nervous system, through the interchange of adaptation and inheritance."[65]

Viewed in this way man is merely a peculiar kind of animal.

This evolutionistic view of man has had a nivellating or leveling effect and has resulted in a loss of critical scientific capacity which has not remained confined to biology. This sometimes led to excesses, undoubtedly not wished by the best representatives of evolutionism. [After all, the "survival of the fittest" does not necessarily mean the survival of the strongest.—Tr.] If man does not differ qualitatively from the animals, then the human "spirit" also must be studied in the light of the soul of the animal. The language of man must be approached from the sounds of animals; there was an evolution of language. The human societies, the nations, must be compared with the associations in the animal kingdom. Wars and the statement that "might is right" can be explained and justified on the basis of the "struggle for life" and the "survival of the fittest." Ideas of "race" and "blood," the institution of concentration camps (natural selection) and the tendency not to trust any more the "gray old age" with the leadership of political parties, churches and the like, are equally so many results of this evolutionism.

We should realize fully that we are dealing here with a *doctrine,* with a *dogma.* This is also evident from the fact that when this interpretation was embraced for the first time there had not yet been found any *Pithecanthropus, Sinanthropus,* etc.

To illustrate our point of view clearly, we have to lay emphasis upon the *characteristic of man.* In our previous chapter we came to the conclusion than an animal is constituted out of three individuality-structures, namely, that of the physico-chemical substrata,

---

[65] E. Haeckel, *Natürliche Schöpfungsgeschichte,* 3rd Ed., 1872, p. 636.

that of the typical biotic functions and that of the psychic behavior. In the animal these are entertwined in the "body" in a hierarchial fashion. Each one of these individuality-structures is governed by special and irreducible laws, but they are interlocked from the bottom to the top.

We then saw that in systematics often only the dead form is taken into consideration, without taking account of the typical biotic phenomena, nor of the typical behavior. We gave clear examples of the fundamental importance of this structural idea by pointing to the species of *Limax* (See p. 135) that are built nearly identically, but that differ in the behavior of mating, and to the willow-warbler and the chiffchaff which one can identify virtually only by its entirely different song.

Such hierarchical individuality-structures we can also differentiate in the anthropoids and in man. In this connection it is of advantage to go a little deeper into the structures of man.

Usually man is split into two independent parts: the *body* which comprises the material part studied in morphology and physiology, and the *soul* which metaphysically comprises the rational thinking, the feeling and the will. In Catholic and Protestant thought this dualism is often extended into the questions concerning man's origin and future. For example, it is usually thought that a new human being derives his temporal material existence from his parents, while the eternal soul is newly created by God (psycho-creationism). We considered this when we discussed the view of Van Nieuwenhoven (p. 97 f). However, Dooyeweerd has demonstrated that this dualistic view of man ultimately is of Greek origin, retrogressing to the theme of form-matter, and that this as such is nowhere found in the Bible.[66] When Scripture speaks about "soul" or "spirit," which is eternal, then these statements have reference to the *"heart"* of man, out of which are all the issues of life, hence also thinking, willing, etc. Also these functions of man belong to the temporal. Only this heart as the integral centre of all temporal functions is supra-temporal.

All temporal functions together form what Dooyeweerd calls the "body" of man. Only this body is scientifically knowable. It

---

[66] H. Dooyeweerd, *op. cit.*, 1935; *Corresp. bl. v.d. Ver. v. Calv. Wijsbeg.* 7 (5), pp. 133-143, 1942; Cf. also *Phil. Ref.*, 15, 66-139, 1950.

is not an abstract material body, but it forms the totality of all temporal functions.

This human body reveals itself as a complex of four individuality-structures. Each of these operates under its own laws. But they are linked together from below upward. This means that although these structures are localized in definite parts of the human body, an organ never belongs exclusively to one of these structures.

The first individuality-structure we find in the physical-chemical substrata of the body. This structure becomes part of the body only when it is linked to the higher structures of the body.

The second structure is the biotic or the organic-vegetative. Within this structure appear the living cells of many various kinds, with their very different physiological functions. This structure governs the vegetative processes. These comprise as it were the physical-chemical structure by directing and adapting this to the phenomena of life. When the body dies then this structure is liberated and the linkage is lost in a process of disintegration. The biotic structure regulates the molecules and atoms, without destroying their own law and order, in such a way that they are made subservient to the functions of life. Hence it is not correct to speak of living molecules. Only the body is independently alive through the linkage of both structures.

The third structure can be designated as that of the instinctive sense organization. It is founded in the central nervous system in the manner in which we find it clearly in the higher animals (squids, insects, vertebrates) as a highest governing principle that guides the totality of life. This by way of the sense organs supplies the contact with the outside world and, by way of the peripheral nervous system with the aid of the muscles, gives the organism its place in the environment. It thus combines as conductor and as co-ordinator the receptors and the effectors.

The two lower structures are governed by it. This happens in two ways. In the first place by means of the autonomic or vegetative nervous system along a nervous pathway but in the second place, also via the endocrine system along the hormonal pathway.

It is interesting that it appears that both ways have very much in common since the nerves at their nerve-endings give off hormone-like substances, just as in the vertebrates the medulla of the adrenals, which can be viewed as part of the autonomic nervous system. But also in all higher animals there are found in the brain cells which, besides nerve function, also fulfil a hormone-producing function (neurosecretory cells). At the same time, it has become evident that these brain cells (*e.g.,* in the hypothalamus of the Vertebrates, in the pars intercerebralis of the protocerebrum of the insects, and in many parts of the central nervous system of the Crustacea) govern, as it were, the whole endocrine system and, by way of that, the vegetative processes (metabolism in a general sense, reproduction, moulting, pupation, protective coloration, etc.).

The fourth structure Dooyeweerd calls the act-structure of the human body, which reveals itself in the acts, for example, knowing, willing and imagining. This act-structure is founded in the cerebral cortex. It is this highest structure of the body which again, via the rest of the central nervous system, influences all the other individuality-structures. Thus in the specifically human actions it involves the entire body.

Considered from the point of view of this structure-idea of man, the complexity of the question about the phylogenetic relation between man and the anthropoids becomes clearly evident. Because, what data do we possess viewed in this light?

a. The Australopithecinae and the characters discussed above, in which the recent anthropoids and man correspond, point out that there have been animals, and that there still are those, in which the lower three individuality-structures to an important measure correspond with those of man.

b. The researches of Portmann teach us that man in his biotic individuality-structure. in addition to the many similarities, also shows considerable characteristic differences from the recent anthropoids.

c. The same holds true for the psychic individuality-structure.

d. However, man possesses in addition still various functions in the act-structure that supersede those mentioned above and that were characteristically present already at the beginning of the Pleistocene

Epoch, as the cultural objects teach us, thus during the time of the Australopithecinae.

Let us remember the expression of Le Gros Clark: "probably the definition of 'Man' will ultimately have to rest on a functional rather than an anatomical basis, the criteria of humanity being the ability to speak and make tools,"[67] and of Weidenreich: "cultural objects are the only guide as far as spiritual life is concerned."[68]

With these investigators we record a tendency to move in the direction of the idea of individuality-structures.

When we summarize these data we come to the conclusion that similar molars, jaws, long bones, skulls—in short, that similar fossils do not signify necessarily similar beings. The fossil of a chiffchaff surely will be similar to that of a willow-warbler.

Now that the *Australopithecinae* give us a reasonable basis to suppose that there may have lived animals which had the same skeleton as man, this does not yet mean that these beings therefore showed the same biotic, behavior and higher structures as man.

For example, we know nothing of the length of pregnancy, of the condition at birth, of the growth intensity, of the length of life, of the eventual ability to speak, of the eventual thinking and believing of *Australopithecus, Meganthropus, Pithecanthropus, Sinanthropus,* etc., etc.,

Although it is proved that the human skeleton with some human forms (Neanderthalers) was more anthropoid than with us, this does not yet prove that they were more anthropoid in their biotic and behavior structures.

Correspondences in the lower individuality-structures between man and anthropoids do not constitute a "simple fact" with the consequences for the other structures. We can even suppose in an extreme case that there lived adjacent to each other creatures that looked fairly well alike, but of which the one was a characteristic anthropoid and the other a 100 per cent man. The problem about the origin of this typical human is not solved in a single respect

---

[67] W. E. Le Gros Clark, 1952, *op. cit.*, p. 73.
[68] F. Weidenreich, 1948, *op. cit.*, p. 109.

in that way. When we speak of "the life of man" we do not think in the very first place about respiration, growth of bones, about molars and jaws; but we then think exactly about all that in which man distinguished himself from the animals.

However, in forming its judgment, creationism does not think only about the scientific data, but, in reference to this problem about the origin of man, it also asks what the Bible tells us about that. This is as follows: "And God created man in his own image. . ." (Gen. 1:27). "And Jehovah God formed man of the dust of the ground, and breathed into his nostrils the breath of life; and man became a living soul" (Gen. 2:7).

What does this mean? People have often thought that we here should suppose that God modeled man out of dust. This would signify that we have here a technical description of the origin of man.

As we have stated repeatedly, nowhere in Genesis, where the origin is discussed, is it permissible to draw that conclusion. (Still less does this conception square with the opinion that the other organisms have been created out of nothing. The idea that plants and animals were created out of "nothing" and man out of "dust" even degrades man in respect to the other living creatures.)

No, the essence of this communication is again a religious revelation. Here man is told that as a totality he is not eternal and that he is not of divine origin, as many gentiles asserted, but that he "is from the earth, earthly"; after the image of God, it is true, but, nevertheless, earthly. These brief statements at the beginning of the Bible point man to his greatness, but, immediately after that, to his insignificance.

Again, here we may not read into this a scientific statement about the "how" of the origin of man, but only a revelation *that* man owes his existence to creation and that in every respect he is linked with that which has been created. The "dust of the earth," there-fore, does not have to be at all the dust as we find it along the road, existing of grains of sand, dried particles of plants, the spores of unicellular organisms, but it may just as well be all that which is earthly and temporal. This means, keeping in mind for a moment the fact that we cannot use texts for conclusions of that nature, that the possibility definitely is not eliminated here that use was made of an animal, which, as is related a few verses earlier, also is brought forth out of the earth.

One also meets repeatedly the opinion that the breathing in of the "breath of life" points to the introduction of the immaterial typically human "soul" or "spirit." This is pure eisegesis having its origin in the theory of the scholastic-philosophical soul-body differentiation.

Scripture wishes least of all to advance that theory. It is here only concerned with the revelation that God took part in every respect with the formation of man in his totality as a *"living* being." This is evident from Genesis 7 verses 21 and 22, where the destruction of the living creatures during the Flood is described: "And all flesh died that moved upon the earth, both birds, and cattle, and beasts, and every creeping thing that creepeth upon the earth, and every man: all in whose nostrils was the breath of life, of all that was on the dry land, died."

So also Ecclesiastes 3:19: "For that which befalleth the sons of men befalleth the beasts; even one thing befalleth them: as the one dieth, so dieth the other; yea, they all have one breath; and man has no pre-eminence above the beasts."

When we thus place side by side the knowledge which we possess of the higher life of the Primates of the Pleistocene Epoch and the revelation that man has been brought forth within that which has been created, then we may not reject in advance the *possibility* that the genesis of man occurred by way of a being that, at least with respect to the characteristics of its skeleton, was an animal, according to our norms and criteria.

How the operation of the origin of man took place is not revealed to us in Scripture. Also science is not able to answer this question. We are just now beginning to realize that the problem of the origin of man is a much more complicated one than we ever imagined.

Already before data were in hand the *doctrine* of descent, based on materialistic faith, found a solution governed only by chance.

of mutation, selection and adaptation which oversteps all essential limitations. Over against that we place creationism which knows from the Christian faith that all the entities of reality are created and that all phenomena and events of the genesis of man fell under the dominance of the Word of God.

It is interesting to record here the opinion of two American authors who belong to the orthodox Protestant movement which in that country is predominantly and strongly opposed to any trace of evolution, namely, Smalley and Fetzer.[69] These authors, who give evidence that they are excellently informed about the modern state of affairs, in bold lines come to the same conclusions concerning the age and the transformation of man as we have expounded it. Also they see the necessity of a change in ideas within orthodox Protestant circles.

A few short quotations may confirm this. Concerning the transformation they say: "It has been shown, however, that man has not aways looked as he does today. The structural differences between modern man and fossil man are great in many respects."

About the age of man: "There is strong evidence, which is constantly increasing, for the antiquity of man." He lived during the Pleistocene: "Although the absolute dates assigned to the Pleistocene period are admittedly only tentative ones, it does appear from several types of work. . . that these dates are of the right order of magnitude and that several hundred thousand years have been involved in the deposition of Pleistocene strata."[70]

About the criteria regarding being human: "It has been pointed out that mental qualities for fossil man cannot be determined with any remote degree of accuracy. The only evidence for development of mental faculties in fossil man lies in the cultural artifacts associated with the human bones." *"Sinanthropus pekinensis* lived in a cave, and there is a well-developed stone industry associated with the bones. Since *Pithecanthropus* seems of approximately the same level of physical development, it is reasonable to suppose that this hominid type was capable of similar cultural development."

---

[69] W. A. Smalley and M. Fetzer, "A Christian View of Anthropology," in *Modern Science and Christian Faith,* Wheaton, pp. 98-195, 1950.
[70] *Op. cit.,* p. 183.

In that part of their publication in which they summarize the data, they come to the conclusion: "The conclusions given above are based upon data which cannot be ignored. Indeed, any intelligent understanding of human origins and human beings through time must take them into consideration."[71]

Finally, Smalley and Fetzer also enter upon the question concerning the eventual correlation between these data and the text of Genesis. After having discussed and criticized the hypothesis of a "late Adam" they say: "A major alternative to the view of a late Adam outlined above is that of an early Adam. This would appear to harmonize better with the present evidence of great antiquity for fossil man. There are those who hold that the genealogical tables of the Scriptures must refer in their earlier parts at least to other sequences than those of generations, and as there is no definite indication as to when creation took place, Adam could have been very early in point of time. Again, this interpretation may have at least two variations. It is possible that God made the physical bodies in which we live by a developmental process, and that early in time He put an eternal spirit into one of these forms. This is also a theistic and evolutionary view, but must not be confused with mechanical evolution. The other alternative to the late Adam view would be that God created Adam instantaneously at a very early point in time, and since that time the physical form of man has varied considerably in space and time."[72]

Apart from the fact that in this last quotation there is still a strong measure of a scholastic and supra-naturalistic conception of creation, the rendition of the opinion of these Americans demonstrates that the line of thought of a Bible believer who honestly and openly takes notice of the present state of affairs in the field of historical anthropology will advance in a direction which is also advocated here above.

---

[71] *Op. cit.*, p. 184.
[72] *Op. cit.*, p. 186.

CHAPTER SIX

CREATION AND EVOLUTION

In the preceding chapters we have given a survey of the most important data that science has at its disposal today concerning the most cardinal points about the problem of the origin of organisms. We have also presented the lines of thought that have led to the most current interpretations of this problem at the present time. The attempt also has been made at the end of each chapter to determine the attitude of the Christian biologist in regard to these points.

In this last chapter we shall try to set forth the essential difference between the evolutionistic and the creationistic way of thinking, and, in addition, we shall attempt to give a total picture on the basis of the last line of thought.

The data obtained through the investigations of the last century are the following: it can be considered as definite that initially there were no living beings present on the earth, and that today, no really *new* life originates. Hence, according to modern conceptions, life must have made its appearance for the first time at a definite moment or at a definite period of time in the history of the earth. Records about this are entirely unknown to us at this moment. The view that life originated from the lifeless, accordingly, rests upon an extensive concatenation of hypotheses, of which some, according to present opinions, are fairly probable (experiment of Miller, p. 46) ; others, to the contrary, are improbable (appearance of enzymes, fermentation, photosynthesis, respiration, etc.).

Equally unknown to us is the first appearance of the phyla to be differentiated in the flora and fauna, as well as the mutual relation of these phyla. As far as the origin of the classes and other higher categories are concerned we are still largely in the dark, although here, in some instances, the indications are not entirely absent. Finally, the origin of man appears to be a much more complicated problem than was anticipated initially. The relation of the fossil hominid forms is strongly disputed. The criteria to determine what is a human being do not appear to lie in the sphere of the fossils. The only thing about which we are sure is that the species are not fixed and that in the past they have changed to an important extent. Some mechanisms that play a part in these changes are known to us.

Although our knowledge has increased greatly in the last century, the problems also seem to have become larger. The evolution of organisms from lifeless matter up to man has not been proved. It is therefore surely incorrect when Simpson says: "Although many details remain to be worked out, it is already evident that all the objective phenomena of the history of life can be explained by purely materialistic factors."[1]

The expression of Portmann with which we began this book corresponds more with reality, namely, that the evolutionary idea is: "in all its details still ever the object of strong criticism and discussion. . ." and ". . . in its final inferences, on every side, projects beyond the scientific facts into the area of faith."[2]

We must first of all devote some attention to this last element

----

[1] G. G. Simpson, *op. cit.*, 1950, p. 343.
[2] A. Portmann, *op. cit.*, 1951, p. 15.

mentioned by Portmann. According to his view evolutionism contains elements that are important for *faith*.

Sometimes we find a more or less plain acknowledgement of this from evolutionistic authors as, for instance, J. Huxley when he says: "I have always believed . . . in the natural origin of living from non-living matter on this planet."[3]

The question now presents itself to what extent the Christian has in common, or *can* have in common, with the evolutionists' definite views concerning the cardinal questions about the origin of living beings in this world.

This is an important question for the theme of this study. This is particularly significant because many have begun to think, perhaps, in the reading of the preceding chapters that in them, in essence evolutionism is accepted—except only that a little Christian sauce has been poured over it in order, opportunistically, to make it more readily digestible.

The answer to this question can be, first of all, according to our view, that one as Christian, despite the cardinal gaps in our knowledge, principally does not have to have any objection against the general *hypothesis* of a genetic continuity of all living organisms, man not excluded. Also, as Christian, one can most of the time work and think along quietly with the struggle in modern science concerning these gaps in our knowledge.

One will have to be more critical than is and has been customary among investigators. Lamarck did not possess data of the past history of the earth and yet he was already convinced in every detail about the correctness of the evolutionistic method of explanation. Haeckel did not know the ancestors of the molluscs. Nor did he know the fossils of hominid forms. But he imagined that he could already describe them.

But this critical attitude is not an essential point of difference since every non-Christian who is a sober investigator will appreciate the necessity of this critical proposition.

When we propose that one as a Christian does not have to reject a priori the idea of a genetic continuity of the living organisms

---

[3] J. Huxley, *Soviet Genetics and World Science*, London, 1949, p. 88.

and that one can co-operate whole-heartedly in the investigations, then this very fact already shows, according to our view, that the difference between evolutionism and creationism in the first instance does not lie in the sphere of the data, of the investigations, and of the hypotheses. This difference lies deeper because the working hypotheses of the *pur sang* evolutionist are not exclusively attempts to find data and to arrange them, but often include already an element of "certain knowledge," of faith.

It is this element which Portmann designates as "the area of faith."

The *pur sang* evolutionist has incorporated in his worldview— his philosophy, his faith—a few dogmatic truths. We have seen earlier how in Lamarck, Darwin, T. H. Huxley and Haeckel faith in the absolute autonomy of the laws of nature took the place of the Christian faith. With some (*e.g.*, Lamarck, T. H. Huxley) the idea of God, it is true, remained positively as a possibility, but God was for them deistically reduced to an impersonal first cause, "cette première cause," "a pre-existent Being." With others, absolute atheism lies in the background of their thinking. Thus J. Huxley says, "I am philosophically a non-theist."[4]

And with that we approach the core of the unbridgeable controversy between evolutionism and creationism.

With the consistent evolutionist, of course, at the root of his scientific views about the problem of origin lies his faith that God does not exist (atheism), or that there was only an impersonal first cause which started the whole machinery of the world, but who does not concern himself with it any further (deism), or that Nature itself is God (pantheism).

All these views have in common the belief that there is no "personal God." From this it follows that the powers of nature ultimately are entirely autonomous, that the origin of all living beings and of all entities of this reality are caused only by a general evolution which bridged all (apparent) boundaries.

From this it also follows that the "belief" of J. Huxley in the origin of life from lifeless matter is not an opinion at which he arrived inductively, but it is a deduction out of a "faith": atheism.

---

[4] J. Huxley, *Nature*, 163, p. 974, 1949.

This holds that *all* happenings in nature are determined *entirely* autonomically, immanently.

This also means that there is no "higher plan" to which the development of the organisms is confined. Only an aimless collision of energies and individuals in continuous conflict of mutation and selection has brought forth the organisms. We find this clearly described when Simpson announces that the phenomena: "are certainly inconsistent with the existence of a supernal perfecting principle, with the concept of a goal in evolution . . ."[5] According to him the same rule holds for man: "Man is the result of a purposeless and materialistic process that did not have him in mind. He was not planned."[6]

How does Simpson know that so well? It is "evident" that he did not obtain this knowledge in an inductive way. He limited himself just as little as Lamarck to "the confines of a simple observer of nature." It is plain that these expressions are nothing else but repercussions in science of his materialistic philosophy, of his "faith."

Creationism, of which the adherents do believe in a personal God and in the history of origin according to plan, distances itself from this evolutionistic method of interpretation and explanation of the origin of organisms.

On the other hand, we have set forth repeatedly that we also put ourselves at a distance from the more or less scholastic and fundamentalistic solutions disseminated extensively in Christian circles.

This requires a further clear explanation because most evolutionists think that when one rejects the core of their view, he definitely has to believe that God from time to time, in a supernatural way, has to intervene in the history of origins, while the adherents of this last view think that one who cannot unite himself with this view should be stamped, preferably, as an evolutionist.

For that reason we give the following exposition: With all questions of detail we started with the supposition that for the Christian there cannot be any consideration of an autonomous evolution from the one into the other. To the contrary, we have

---

[5] G. G. Simpson, *op. cit.*, 1950, p. 262.
[6] *Op. cit.*, 1950, p. 344.

emphasized that all changes fall under the power of God's dominance and direction.

The danger is that one is going to isolate the problem of the origin of plant and animal types and of man from the totality of the natural processes by positing that through a sudden specific supernatural interference of God the origin of such novae could be explained. This includes, for instance, that it could be supposed that in the pre-Cambrian suddenly a living force was introduced by God into the world from without, and that in the Cambrian Period suddenly the various types of phyla were made through the momentary action of God, and that at the beginning of the Pleistocene with the formation of man by God all at once there was placed upon the earth either a totally new human being or that the mental qualities in this temporal reality were introduced from the outside (see the view of Smalley and Fetzer, p. 199).

Such a view is advanced in modern biology, for instance, by Hedwig Conrad-Martius.[7] She is strongly under the impression of the inability to deduce historically the types of structural plans and of the fact that modern science begins to notice more and more that the evolutionary changes are, relatively speaking, of a superficial nature. She thinks accordingly that non-Christian science ultimately will have to accept the view that initially a primeval organism originated that held within itself potentially the structural possibilities of all that developed from it later. Her judgment concerning this is: . . . "such a primeval organism, which held within itself potentially the whole living world, would be the miracle of all miracles."[8] Hence she considers creation the only possibility for the explanation of the origin of the vegetable and the animal kingdoms. "And, indeed, creation in the original sense, a production not merely of form, but also of matter. Since, however, the adoption of the idea of such a primeval organism, pregnant, so to speak, with the organic life of the whole world, and thus only having to unfold itself like a single organism, is an absurdity, pursuant to all the facts and arguments set forth in this book, one must accept the original idea of creation, the production

---

[7] H. Conrad-Martius, *Abstammungslehre*, München, 1949.
[8] *Op. cit.*, p. 347.

of a world of organisms differentiated 'from the very beginning' and gradated.'"[9]

She differentiates, further, between the "typical" and the "derivative" types. The former are the fundamental structural types. They came into existence through creation. " 'Typical' types did not originate by concrete happenings, but were creatively realized according to an essential idea of formation: the organisms representing these types are in a real sense 'formed' corresponding to fundamental types."[10]

The "derivative types" originated purely within nature upon the basis of the "typical types" through the processes of mutation, etc. They do not rest upon "fundamental but on 'accidental' ideas." However, we should not interpret this as if the latter were not included in the "plan of creation." "Nothing is further from the truth. Both kinds of types, indeed, every single individual corresponds to an idea of creation and is the realization of this idea of creation. In the 'eternal Word,' the Logos, all fundamental and accidental ideas are contained, and the latter and the former, in conformity with the order of essence to which they belong, are 'put to work': the former through the direct 'formation' or 'impress' of the organisms concerned, conformable to the essential idea of form, which with the act of creation became, in the organisms, an 'inner form-giving potentiality' (Dacqué), a qualitative genetical groundwork (Ungerer), The latter originated by means of natural-empirical causes (direct action, mutation, orthogenesis, reconstructive regulation of the disturbed biological balance, which requires new adaptation), which, according to the virtual potentialities added initially to the organisms formed as fundamental types, produced the derivative types. Here living nature reveals itself as form-changing and type-creating."[11] Both types are thus "original 'ideas of creation' of God."

From these few quotations it is clear that Conrad-Martius favors a modern continuation of the scholastic line of the form-matter scheme of the "ideas of creation" (ante rem, in re), which leads to dualistic views in the case of questions concerning structure, but also with the problem of origin.

---

[9] *Op. cit.*, pp. 347-348.
[10] *Op. cit.*, p. 351.
[11] *Ou. cit.*, p. 352.

This solution, it is clear, issues from a twofold action in time on the part of God, namely, a general maintenance and an elaboration of that which is already present in time and from a dated supernatural intervention of God. This does not only destroy the immanent unity of all that which has been created, which unity then can be found only in the plan of God's creation as the totality of the ideas of creation, but, above all, it drags the creation down into time so that we can point *where* and *when* God created, and *how* God acted and *what* has been produced through this action.

However, the divine operation on the one hand does not permit itself to be scientifically discovered, indicated, dated and localized within reality, but, as we have contended previously, it escapes exactly in every respect our instruments. The creation is not periodically introduced into temporal reality, but it has produced, precisely through the power of God, this reality as a totality bound by time. Creation preceded time.

On the other hand, we may not introduce into God's transaction a dualism which seems to simplify our problems, since in that way we reduce God to an instrument of our thinking, a *deus ex machina* that we call to our aid to help us solve the critical points in our thinking.

This last idea we find clearly in O. Kühn: "When, now, the supposition of an act of creation for the oldest living beings is considered necessary because of conclusive grounds, in case one does not prefer to renounce every explanation and to register only facts, then also the living beings that appeared later must be explained upon the basis of the intervention by metaphysical factors."[12]

The same reasoning we find in the important work of Ramm: " . . . the geological record does not reveal a continuity, an evolution, but . . . it reveals great gaps. Animal forms appear suddenly. The geologist writes: 'form X appears in the Devonian.' The theologian informs him that from the theological vantage point the word *appeared* is to be rendered *created*." " . . . additional forms have been created in the history of the earth." "We believe in several acts of fiat creation in the history of the earth. . . "[13]

---

[12]O. Kühn, *Die Deszendenztheorie*, München, 1951, p. 67.
[13] B. Ramm. *op. cit.*, 1955, pp. 116, 228.

After renouncing the evolutionistic and the scholastic opinions, we shall try to find a *direction* in which possibly a solution can be found for the difficulties mentioned. Let us orient ourselves here with a series of articles published by Diemer, a zoologist who, alas, perished in German captivity.[14]

Diemer approached the question of creation and evolution from the general problem of the *miracle,* so that it is placed in a much broader relation. We follow first of all, very briefly, Diemer's historical review of the conceptions of the miracle in western thought. He begins with St. Augustine. Already in the chapter about the origin of life we saw that he was of the opinion that all things were created by God in the beginning in conformity with divine ideas, and, particularly, as concrete germs and causes which could unfold themselves in an evolutionary process in time. This idea of St. Augustine is linked with his opinion that a sharp distinction must be made within God's activity with that which had been created between the creation comprising the six "days of creation" as an entity and providence that became joined to it thereupon. We stated already that this opinion included an explanation of the phenomenon of spontaneous generation. But also, for instance, the origin of man fell under the same theme. Adam initially was created in principle. Only after the divine creation man became visible by way of the law and order according to which in time actualities originate from protentialities. In the beginning God had given matter the necessary potency from which thus, only after creation, man in the course of time could be formed.

When we then notice how Augustine thought about miracles, then it appears clearly, according to Diemer, that he did not consider these as contranatural. They transpire only contrary to the order known to us, as this appears to us from the ordinary occurrences in nature. However, they are not in conflict with the "highest law of nature" of the world-plan of God because they are precisely contained in it.

[14] J. H. Diemer, Letter to the Editor, *De Standaard,* 20 Febr. 1939: "De totaliteit van het leven," *Calvinistisch Weekblad,* 6. pp 78 and 86, 1940; "De 'dagen' in het scheppingsverhaal," *Calvinistisch Studentenblad,* 6, (3), pp. 1-6, 1942; "Natuur en Wonder," *Philosophia Reformata,* 8, pp. 100-128, 1943; 9, pp. 42-61, 1944; "Natuur en Wonder," *Org. v.d. Chr. Ver. v. Nat. en Geneesk, in Ned.,* pp. 53-92, 1944.

Diemer is accordingly of the opinion that in Augustine there is to be found little support for the view of the so-called supranaturalism, the theory that God in time intervenes supernaturally in certain cases. It is true, he has objections against Augustine's idea of providence. Augustine states correctly that it is God who unfolds the entire created reality, but he tied this idea to the realistic neo-platonism with the rational germs and causes, by means of which the development is reduced to an unfolding of material forms through rational powers of formation acting upon an unformed condition at the beginning. Hence, things are made from unformed material through rational forms.

This latter element we find more emphatically in medieval scholasticism, particularly in Thomas Aquinas, through which also a supranaturalistic view of the miracle originated. The natural order of the specifically determined causes in its entirety is the same as divine providence. This order now is so constituted that every cause can be limited in its action by a higher one. This opens the possibility for the miracle as the result of an interposition of the Highest Cause in the created order. On the one hand, a miracle seems to be contrary to nature. However, there exists a natural receptivity on the part of that which has been created for the action of higher causes. On the other hand, according to Aquinas, the miracles in a certain sense do belong to the supernatural world-order. In the case of a miracle God intervenes in a way that transcends nature, whereby, however, something natural comes into existence. As far as the cause and purpose are concerned, the miracle belongs to the supernatural; according to the results it belongs to nature.

The core of Diemer's criticism of this view reads: "The direct action of God in nature is confined in the Thomistic supernaturalism to the momentary action of the First Cause in case of the miracles. The ordinary progress of things is executed by God only indirectly, namely, by means of 'nature.' God's providential direction of the world, concerning which Scripture speaks repeatedly, Thomas identifies with a realistically conceived natural order and is thus robbed of its miraculous character."[15]

---

[15] J. H. Diemer, *op. cit.*, 1943, p. 128.

This scholastic conception of nature and the miracle was continued in Reformation theology. This was not the case with Calvin and Luther, who have not occupied themselves theoretically with this question. But it was true of their immediate followers in the seventeenth and eighteenth centuries. According to this scholasticism the miracles are separate interventions of God in the regular course of nature, whereby natural laws are suspended in a supernatural way.

During the seventeenth century the Roman Catholic and Protestant conception of the miracle was fought by rationalism. This viewed nature as a closed system of material causes which autonomically, by law and order, determined the happenings. With Spinoza the laws of nature are decisions of the will of God. This means that if God should perform miracles that run counter to natural laws, God would be acting contrary to the order which He himself instituted, which would be absurd according to Spinoza. It is thus impossible for the miracle to exist, and when we imagine that we observe a miracle then that means that we are not (yet) able to explain the phenomenon concerned. Hence, with Spinoza nature becomes absolutely autonomous. The laws of nature are eternally necessary and true. There was no creation: with him nature becomes identified with God (pantheism).

Leibniz does not identify God with nature. God, as the supernatural cause, created nature initially. He is thus the First Cause who is substantially to be distinguished from nature. With Leibniz we find deism united with supranaturalism. Reality operates purely mechanically according to the created laws. A supernatural *regulatory* intervention of God is out of the question. He does recognize the possibility of the miracle as an intervention of God above the powers of nature, which is unacceptable to reason but acceptable to faith. However, these miracles correspond to the general plan of the world.

Leibniz' conception resembles much that of Thomas Aquinas. The latter, however, was a realist and distinguished substantial forms and a material substrate to reality; the former was nominalist and differentiated no general but individual substances, the monads,

by means of which he defended an entirely different idea concerning the structure of nature (*lex continui*, etc., see pp. 62-64).
Just as a mathematician works according to general theorems, so
there are general ordered regulations in nature which should be
attributed to the modes of operation of God. And, just as the
mathematician uses higher suppositions in instances in which the
ordinary ones are not sufficient, so too the miracles are attributable
to a concatenation of supernatural acts of God. The ordinary laws
as well as the miracles are subsumed under the harmonia universalis,
just as mathematical propositions are produced through one and the
same reason. Therefore, the miracle is thus rationalized by
Leibniz.

Briefly, Diemer points out that in Kant, who viewed nature
as the reality of experience, as an entirely closed system of
mechanical laws determined by reason, there is no question about
miracles. Kant combats the supernatural belief in miracles, but
also the apparent compromise constructed by the rationalistic deists.

The most radical consequences concerning the problem of
nature and miracles were drawn by the materialistic natural
philosophy of the nineteenth and twentieth centuries. Diemer
gives a few impressive quotations:

Thus from Büchner: "There is nothing miraculous. All that
happens, what has happened and what shall happen, happens, has
happened and shall happen in a *natural* way; that means, in a way
which is only stipulated by an orderly co-operation or concurrence
of the eternally present matter and the powers of nature or motions
connected therewith. . . . Before the eyes of science all miracles are
similar, that is, the result of an uncontrolled phantasy in relation
with a profound ignorance of the laws of nature."

Similar expressions are to be found also in Haeckel. With him
the root of everything is "the all-embracing law of substance, the
great law of the conservation of matter and energy," together with
the law of natural evolution. The Christian belief in creation is
done for: "The modern doctrine of evolution has convinced us
that such a 'creation' never occurred, that the universe exists from
eternity, and that the law of substance rules everything."

It is these materialistic considerations that also today form the undertow of the opposition of modern science to the concept of the miracle.

In an interesting way Diemer shows how in recent orthodox Protestant thought the supernaturalistic view of the miracles is generally held, and, more particularly, as a kind of superstructure based upon a rationalistic view of nature. According to rationalism nature is a functional reality in time confined within itself. The investigator has to proceed from sense perception and, hence, can deal only with laws, forces and possibilities which can be known through research. Only that provides knowledge because only the works of nature that are founded in reason can be known. Whatever goes beyond that is the object of faith.

Supranaturalism now sees that the miracles that are recorded in Scripture cannot be explained by means of the laws and forces which rationalistic investigation has discovered. Rather, they are in conflict with that. Since one wishes to hold on to the miracles anyway, one then seeks his escape in the idea of the supernatural intervention of God whereby thus definite natural laws are "derived," "broken," "raised," "suspended." It is Diemer's definite conviction that all these supranaturalistic views issue from an approach to the biblical miracles with the aid of the thinking-apparatus of a non-Christian philosophy.

With the expounding of his own view he therefore, first of all, starts by perusing what the Bible describes as "nature" and "miracle." Surprising data result from this.

About "nature" itself Scripture speaks very seldom. Rather, there is mention of the "ordinances" of the heavens, for the sun, moon, stars, for the waters, the rain, wind, the creatures, man. All these ordinances have been instituted by God. They are subsumed under the world-order of God, which has been created and is sustained through the divine Word.

This created world-order Diemer calls nature. "It is not a 'material world,' which would possess a certain independence over against God. To the contrary, nature is the *order of creation,* functioning in total dependence upon God."[16]

And now *everything* happens in accordance with this divine world-order instituted in time. Nowhere in Scripture, in definite situations or with particular miracles, is there mention of "abrogation," "suspension" or "destruction" of this order. Nor does Scripture mention "supernatural" phenomena which would occur through divine intervention in nature. According to Scripture, God does not work alongside nature, for instance, by making God appear supernaturally when the "forces of nature" are inadequate. "All power is God's power and through it the totality of all things is made in the act of creation and is sustained and unfolded in the course of time according to the instituted world-order. Now, this order of things is what we call nature, and this nature is a miraculous work of God."[17]

And when Diemer in connection with this asks, what according to Scripture are the miracles, then he circumscribes them as "the incomprehensible deeds and the unsearchable ways of God in the facts of creation, providence and recreation." The Bible designates these miracles as, for example, wonderful deeds, wonderful works, marvelous things, miraculous signs, powers, etc. They have reference to that which has been created, as a witness of God's majesty, but at the same time to divine providence, from which nothing in heaven and on earth is removed; and, finally, they also have reference to the deliverance from all distress. All these miracles have a common center: "The wisdom wherewith God has made everything marvelous is the same with which He sustains everything, directs it and leads it to completion."

The centering of all these miracles is directed, according to Scripture, upon Jesus Christ: "In Christ Jesus is revealed *the* miracle of God's concern with the world. From this central miracle the miracles of creation, providence and recreation may not be separated."[19]

Subsequent to that Diemer discusses in succession these three forms of the miracle. First, the miracle of creation. We can experience that in the majesty, wealth and orderliness in created

---

[16] J. H. Diemer, *op. cit.,* 1943, p. 101.
[17] *Ibid.,* p. 101.
[19] *Ibid.,* p. 103.

nature. In a sinless nature this would have been the ordinary attitude of man. "Fallen man, as a rule, does not see God any more in the regular course of nature, but at best in the extra-ordinary phenomena and incomprehensible occurrences. He then speaks of 'miracles' which must have come into existence through divine intervention and makes a distinction between these 'miracles' on the one hand and nature which would be comprehensible, on the other hand. Or, in other words, between the creative act of God and providence. But in this way both acts are distorted. The miracle is placed outside of nature and nature is deprived of its miraculous character."[20]

His treatise contains two important cores that are of a decisive significance for our further exposition. The first he formulates as follows: "God's creative act does not have its beginning and end in cosmic time, but, precisely, calls this duration of time with its order into existence."[21]

The second important core is a corollary to this, namely, that the creation should be viewed as a "single, unrepetitive" act of divine creation, through which this entire reality, in all its structures, has been produced.

Therefore, he also sees Genesis 1, following St. Augustine, as a communication adapted to our faith. Our faith functions in time. That is why in describing creation, which is prior to all time, it is depicted in the form of a temporal order. "Only when God's act of creation which did not take place in time is set forth in a temporal order, can faith obtain insight into the structure and the direction of this."[22]

Genesis also shows that the Word of God is the absolute beginning of all that has been created. In this respect all kingdoms of nature constitute one whole. Man is the highest creature, since in him all the structures of temporal reality are united. In man all nature is directed to the service of God. The creation of this reality as a totality, accordingly, preceded time. "Only then has the moment arrived when the process of unfolding can begin in cosmic time and the providence of God becomes operative."[23]

[20] *Ibid.,* pp. 103, 104.
[21] *Ibid.,* p. 104.
[22] *Ibid.,* p. 104.
[23] *Ibid.,* p. 105.

"When the unfolding in time begins before the eye of our spirit, the act of creation is finished, completed."[24]

He then further points out that evolutionism, which thinks that it can derive the one fundamental structure from the other, is in conflict with the Bible. But this is also true of the supranaturalism that teaches "that God repeatedly, with the appearance of new specific structures in the cosmic process of time, has intervened supernaturally in the happenings in nature. When, in the course of time, we notice that suddenly new forms and figures make their appearance in the various kingdoms in nature, in other words, when new structures come to realization, we then may not separate these from the created totality, in which they were already contained. *Before us* they become suddenly *visible* but they are not suddenly made by God. They do not come at a definite moment from outside or from beyond into time."[25]

This leads us to the second type of miracle, that of providence. This we find in the process of unfolding: ". . . the entire cosmic process of unfolding is governed by divine providence and directed to the completion at the end of time. Through His omnipotent and omnipresent wisdom and power God holds continuously in existence the created world-order from the time of His rest after the labor of the six days of creation. The cosmic process of unfolding cannot be separated from the creation-week, nor from the creation in the beginning; in other words, just as little from the created order as from the totality. Because in the totality lay contained all that which would be made visible in the "week" that has been mentioned and during the succeeding course of time."[26]

The reflection of this providence we see in the very small to the very pronounced harmonic relations which are all directed to the coming of the Kingdom of God. This also holds true for the life of man. Conspicuous occurrences should not be viewed as interventions of God from above, but as natural processes subject to divine providence, although we, for the rest, can experience them as signs of this.

---

24 *Orgaan Chr. Ver.*, etc., 1944, p. 63.
25 *Phil. Ref.*, 8, p. 105.
26 *Ibid.*, pp. 105-106.

The same line of thought Diemer sets forth in regard to the problem of the "answer to prayer." "When a recovery follows a fervent prayer, or if a prayer is answered in another way, then there is nothing that is above or contrary to the natural order of things. But the answer to prayer may be a sign for the believer of the miracle of the providence of the living God. There is here not a 'supernatural' intervention, but through the guidance of faith what happens is directed into definite channels, that would not have happened without prayer and faith. The prayer is answered only when what is requested is subservient to the coming of the Kingdom of God."[27]

And with that we approach the third type of miracle, that of re-creation. In correspondence with the created order the lower entities are instituted for the service of the higher. We saw this in a previous chapter. The lower entities function according to their own laws, but in that they can be subject harmoniously to the higher entities, as with the higher animals the behavior aspect dominates and guides all lower functions.

We find this structural plan also in man. Here it is the function of faith that gives supreme guidance. Created man lived initially in such a way that the function of his faith was in complete agreement with God's mandate to unfold all forces and potentialities laid in creation according to His plan. "He obeyed the Word of God and, in him, all nature, which followed his guidance. All happenings in nature were directed to the service of the Kingdom of God."[28]

Through the Fall man, and with him the whole cosmos, lost this direction so that all the functions of that which was created began to act destructively and disintegratingly. In Jesus Christ, God has given creation again a new principle. Through this the direction toward the Kingdom of God is again restored. In Him God has redeemed the world from sin and destruction. This Kingdom of God has to be realized in time through the conflict with sin and its results.

In this central miracle lies the "explanation" of the miracles of

---

[27] *Ibid.*, p. 106.
[28] *Ibid.*, p. 109.

re-creation that we find in the institution and the maintenance of the Church, in conversion, but also in the "miraculous signs" such as Christ's stilling of the storm or his changing of water into wine. These miraculous signs show us the original power which man possesses over nature. No abrogation or break-through of physical laws takes place . . . but there is a sovereign dominance over these laws. Just as little are laws abrogated in the healings of Christ, but disturbances and retardations of what normally happens."[29]

These potentialities are given to man within the sphere of nature with faith as the guiding and dominating function. Or as Christ says: "For verily I say unto you, If ye have faith as a grain of mustard seed, ye shall say unto this mountain, Remove hence to yonder place; and it shall remove; and nothing shall be impossible unto you" (Matt. 17:20).

It is not necessary for the discussion of our problem that we relate the sequence of Diemer's treatise on the miracle. One can consult for further documentary evidence the literature recorded. What has been related is sufficient to show clearly how Diemer abandoned radically the idea of a divine intervention during the genesis of flora and fauna, since this idea, according to his opinion, arose from a mixture of Rationalism and scholastic-Greek opinions. At the same time it must have been apparent that he derived his main ideas from Scripture.

We, therefore, gladly follow him in his views. It is also entirely in line with the conclusions of our first chapter, namely, that Scripture does not give us scientific facts, but when we listen faithfully, it gives us the main lines of the most general world and life view.

Diemer has made it plain to us what it is that we are concerned about anent the problem of "Creation and Evolution," namely, the very general question concerning God's operation in this world. And we Christians have ever been inclined, where we stumble over occurrences incomprehensible to our minds, to see the hand of God suspending natural laws in the "miracles." We saw that in the explanations about the origin of the groups of animals and with the occurrences which we call "miraculous signs." Constantly

---

[29] *Ibid.*, p. 110.

God has been invoked by us as a "deus ex machina" at the places where we could use Him.[30]

The generality of this problem is evidenced by the corresponding method whereby the science of history wrestles with this question. In an interesting treatise Smit[31] has pointed out how on the part of the Christians it was seen that the general course of history is determined by immanent laws, but that with special occurrences they thought that they could see "the hand of God." For many Christians "prosperity remained a blessing, reversal a punishment, and that which was striking and surprising were the most marked elements of their view concerning the hand of God."

However, when we notice that the jumbling together of creation and providence does not fit with reality, but that only one creation in the beginning is followed by providence then we can see the problems more sharply. These are of two kinds:

1. The first we can designate as that of the origin of new entities: life, the psyche, the mental capacities. These are created in the beginning, but only later do they come under the guidance of God, as it were under the echo of His creative Word, for the unfolding within the incomprehensible miracle of the created totality.

This means that we as Christians should not consider it impossible that life originated *by way* of lifeless matter. Hence, we do not have to be at all opponents of the hypothesis of probionts and the like. But we should offer resistance to the view that this life in all its aspects can be reduced to physical-chemical laws, since it is a created entity of reality.

One can object that something cannot exist definitely before it is present in concrete form and, hence, that our reasoning is a playing with words. Therefore, we give the following illustration which, as all imagery, is askew: with the realization of a concert we have to distinguish between a composer, a composition, a conductor, an orchestra and a performance.

When we listen to the radio we only hear the performance. As

---

[30] For a more theological treatise of the problem concerning the immediate and the mediate action of God in this world and at the time of creation, see the informative article of L. Verduin, *"Toward a Theistic Creationism,"* in *Geloof en Wetenschap*, 54, 183-198, 1956; Grand Rapids, 1957, Baker.

[31] M. C. Smit, *Het Goddelijke geheim in de geschiedenis*, 1955.

scientists only the data of fragments of the performance are at our disposal. The Christian knows that before the performance began there was a Composer who made the composition (the divine plan of this world) and that an orchestra was organized (the creation of the order and the entities) and, besides, that during the performance the conductor directs it all (divine providence).

The materialist who listens to the radio and, very much perturbed, catches a few sounds, concludes that it is "evident" that these "are certainly inconsistent with the existence of a supernal perfecting principle," that there surely is no "goal" in this music, that it can only be explained as a "not-planned, purposeless and materialistic process." Since he does not wish to accept the orchestra as given, he comes to the conclusion that the oboe-sound suddenly or gradually came from the sounds of the violin.

The Christian, because of a wonderful revelation (Scripture), has been able to look behind the screen.

This picture can clear up much of the confusion of the discussion between Christians and non-Christians, and among Christians mutually, about the problems with which we are confronted in this book.

In the first place, the Christian is just as little musically inclined as the evolutionist, and definitely does not pretend to possess a better radio. He thus has the same sound (data) at his disposal and he too has to construct working hypotheses in order to try to form unity in the sounds. Also among the non-Christian listeners there are advocates of the idea that we should be on the lookout for differences in sound that *in origine* are not to be reduced to one another (entities); but by other non-Christians it is pointed out to them that this idea is inconsistent and cannot be proved strictly from the sounds. The Christian surmises, but only upon the basis of his faith, that there are indeed essential differences in the sounds. Whether the one or the other opinion is correct is difficult to prove, probably never to be proved with the apparatus we have.

Also the primary origin has this element of unprovability, because, seated before the radio, it is strictly not possible to prove the existence of a composer, nor of a score, nor of an orchestra, nor of a conductor.

The "non-believer" denies this radically and raises the objection that the Christian is unscientific when he thinks he should persist in this attitude. The "believer" knows for sure that he is right and considers that the "unbeliever's" opinion rests upon a much more "miraculous" faith than his.

Now we shall discuss the opinions of the Christians among one another. The supranaturalists think that when suddenly there is the sound of trumpets that this is the result of trumpeters that suddenly came into existence out of nothing. According to them the stage of the creation becomes filled only gradually. Although, on the one hand, they accept a score they come to the conclusion that now and then improvisations occur. That is why there originates with them a conflict between the composer and the conductor.

With Diemer, and we join hands with him, composer and conductor are one, and the whole orchestra is constituted from the beginning.

This picture may have elucidated why we do not have to reject the idea of a continuous connection between the living and life-less. The same holds, for example, with the origin of man. Also with this problem we may not reject in advance the possibility that there has existed a genetic relation between man and animal. The human "mental capacities," however, are not to be traced back to the animal psyche. They function within the entities of reality created in the beginning. How this eventual development from animal to man transpired is not known to us. Nor do we know how and where and when these "mental capacities" have been realized. These are questions that perhaps belong to the sphere of science. We should not detach ourselves from these problems as if we already have the solutions, but we have to occupy ourselves with them among all other investigators.

Perhaps it is superfluous, but in order to prevent misconception it must be pointed out that we do not mean to say that, for instance, a mother gorilla all at once gave birth to a human infant. That would be an absurdity. Man is in all his structures a unity and for that reason we should much rather suppose that within that which has been created and, specifically, within the group of higher mammals, a separate line led to man, a line in which all lower structures were directed at the unfolding of the higher structures of man. We are strengthened in this conception since, although man in as far as his bones, cells and blood are concerned, displays a great concurrence with the higher animals, in other, namely the higher functions of lower order (see the previous chapter), he differs considerably from these animals.

2. The second problem that is of great importance in this view is the question to what extent the divine guidance and governance of these processes is possible within this once-created reality. This is the problem of the biologist-creationist but also, for example, of the Christian historian.

The extreme solutions are, first, of deism which holds that the divine guidance can be executed only out of the "harmonia praestabilita" by way of the immutable, absolutely determined causal laws of nature; and, secondly, those of the ones who would presume that there are no generally valid natural laws, but that God from moment to moment creates new situations from above. This last conception signifies, according to scientific standards, chaos, however absurd this may sound.

Upon the basis of what we have sketched above neither the one nor the other view is acceptable. Or, to stay with our comparison, according to this point of view, neither the composer nor the conductor may be negated.

Proceeding from this, the only conclusion that can be drawn, at least for our human thinking, is that our current notion of orderly relations and of the nature of laws does not correspond with reality.

The idea of a divine intervention, in the case of the Protestant scholastics, as Diemer has set forth, came from the acceptance of the causally inviolability of the laws of nature. When these now should not be of the nature of a completely single-line determinism, would not then the possibility of variation make this at least somewhat more comprehensible for us who believe that God guides the processes along a mediate way?

Smit in his publication mentioned above seeks a similar direction. He also rejects the idea of a sudden intervention from above and of the one-line course of the relations within the creation. He reasons as follows: "It begins to appear probable that the connection between cause and action, that the conditioning in the broadest sense is wrapped in a mystery, although before the consciousness of many there is here no mystery, but at most an incompleteness present in our knowledge. According to our view, the separation between cause and action can be the source of the divergence in the explanations of a phenomenon: the multiplicity of opinions is possible not only because of the complexity of a phenomenon, but especially because the lines which unite the factors with the result, run through an area where cause becomes transformed into action. . .

"Summarizing we conclude: in the transformation from causes into the result, in the transition from influence to result, lies the possibility for the result and for the consequence—I speak constantly anthropomorphically—to be liberated from the force of circumstances."[32]

Now, we can place this problem in sharp relief only when in the science of history as well as in biology, we trace its source. As far as biology is concerned we are close when we once more repeat the quotation from T. H. Huxley: "The one act of faith in the convert to science is the confession of the universality of order and of the absolute validity, in all times and under all circumstances, of the law of causation."

Our faith in the divine guidance in all that happens in this reality is hampered in the deepest sense by this presupposition which already by the astute Huxley was designated as a pure *act of faith* to the *confession* of which we should permit ourselves to be *converted*.

This faith in the absolute single-line determinateness of that which happens in nature arose as a result of the great successes achieved in astronomy, natural science and mechanics through the mathematical description of the phenomena. And the Christian who had adopted this faith could thus see the divine management of this reality only as a breaking-through of this iron control.

---

[32] *Op. cit.*, p. 26.

Hence, in the last century people proceeded from the assumption that all occurrences in physical nature must be viewed as causally determined in a single line. This means that through the condition in a physical system at a definite moment all the succeeding situations are entirely determined.

This physical "confession" was introduced thereupon by the evolutionists in biology, by others in psychology and also in the science of history. This apotheosis of the physical laws ("everything happens . . . in a way which is stipulated only by an orderly co-operation or occurrence of the eternally present matter and the forces of nature or motions connected therewith") is unacceptable to the Christian who believes in the eternal God as *Creator* and *Ruler* of this *temporal* reality. The newer research in physics after the atomic processes has brought to light that this deterministic view of causality is definitely incorrect. Or, as Sizoo says: "Even from the most profound level, from which the modern explanation of physical phenomena takes its point of departure, the level of the fundamental particles, the principle of causality of classical physics is being discarded because of the observations themselves."[33]

Physical research thus comes to the conclusion that instead of a deterministic causality, a statistical form of causality ultimately dominates the physical phenomena: "The observable changes in condition which transpire within a microstructure are *possible* processes, not *necessary* processes. The moments when they shall take place are unpredictable."[34]

The experimental biologist knows that in the living organisms there are many laws that are of a statistical nature; indeed, that some can even be traced back to these primary atomic probabilities.

At the end of his publication Sizoo points out that the deterministic belief made itself guilty of an unpermissible crossing of boundaries since it concluded from causality to the impossibility of the miracle, "as if created man can ever deduce from his observation of the created world what the Creator is *not* able to do."

On the other hand, says Sizoo: ". . . . it also testifies to the overestimation of scientific knowledge when, as often happens in

---

[33] G. J. Sizoo, *De herziening van het physische causaliteitsbeginsel*, 1952, pp. 13-14; *Cf.* also P. Groen, *Over de grenzen der voorspelbaarheid in de natuur*, 1952.
[34] *Ibid.*, p. 16.

the discussion of the revision of the principle of causality in Christian circles, the *possibility* of the miracle is concluded from the statistical character of the predictable."[35]

This is an expression worthy of consideration, because how strong is the tendency for the investigator of nature to rejoice when he has finally found some little holes among the fixed laws of nature where he can admit divine guidance in his thinking. The miracle, however, is not a scientifically verifiable occurrence, but can be accepted only through faith and established as such.

However, this does not remove two important matters. First, that with the breaking through of the deterministic faith, "the one act of faith in the convert to science," the temptation to the faith of the Christian from the supposed proof of the impossibility of the divine rule of this world has fallen away. And in the second place, it is of importance that the Bible believer who, as we saw in the discussion of Diemer's publications, proceeds from the principle that the eventual rectilinear laws of the lower entities, in many miracles, are made subservient to the higher, realizes that with many other miraculous signs which are related to us in Scripture, it is precisely the *improbability* that makes that which happens for us as a *sign* of miraculous divine guidance, without thereby *explaining* it. In other words, it means that God, who has created all rectilinear or non-rectilinear laws and sustains and rules them from moment to moment, does not have to be limited to a *possibility* that has been designated by us; but, among others, does make use of this way of (according to human experience) improbability.

Many of the ten plagues of Egypt (for example, hail, gnats, locusts and frogs) are *natural* phenomena which *frequently* occur in that land. The sign of the miracle, however, *for the believer,* was the statistical improbability that they appeared directly upon the command of Moses (Exodus 7 and following chapters). The incidental hand of God was thought to be present here by the supranaturalistically believing Egyptian scientists: "Then the magicians said to Pharaoh, this is the finger of God" (Exod. 8:19). After it had not rained for three years during the time of Ahab, it was very natural that it rained once again. The sign of a miracle

---

[35] *Ibid.*, p. 19.

for the faithful was, however, that the scientifically very improbable fact happened after the prayer of Elijah, which is described as follows: "And it came to pass in a little while, that the heavens grew black with clouds and wind, and there was a great rain" (I Kings 18:45). It was very common to catch much fish in the Sea of Tiberias, but the sign of a miracle was *for the believer* that, after the disciples for a whole night had taken their "chances" and had not caught anything, immediately after the word of Jesus the net was so brimful that they could not pull it inside the ship (John 21:6).

With all these and similar "improbable" occurrences only the believer can notice and adore divine guidance. For the non-believer they are "coincidences" or they are attributed to unusual knowledge so that one could view Moses only as an excellent biologist who had noticed for a long time that there were many larvae of frogs, and who would regard Elijah as an outstanding meteorologist. The believer, however, must train himself in experiencing the miracle also in the common occurrences.

It is proper here in this last chapter to trace whether the line of thought that we have followed in regard to the problem of origin constitutes a radical break with the views of the classical orthodox thinkers of Reformed persuasion.[36] We confine ourselves here to Abraham Kuyper who in his speech on *"Evolutie"* in 1899 gave evidence of having occupied himself profoundly with this problem. First of all, we shall see what his attitude was in regard to supranaturalism. In an extensive treatise, which we can repeat only partly, Berkouwer deals with this question.[37] It is evident that Kuyper was strongly opposed to supranaturalism, especially since it proceeds from the view that nature assumes a certain force of independence over against God. We can best reiterate Kuyper's reasoning by citing a part of Berkouwer's treatise, which abounds with a great number of quotations from Kuyper's work.

After having pointed out Kuyper's rejection of the idea of the independency of nature, Berkouwer continues: "This shows itself strongest in the supranaturalistic view of the miracle. One views

---

[36] Compare in this connection also the instructive article of P. G. Berkhout, *Revelation and Evolution, Geloof en Wetenschap*, 55, pp. 166-176, 1957.

[37] G. C. Berkouwer, *De voorzienigheid Gods*, Kampen, 1950, pp. 229ff.

then the miracle as a divine intervention *now* and *then* in the ordinary course of things. Everything runs according to law and to a fixed order (nature), 'but occasionally there appears a mysterious hand that intervenes in this clockwork and which suddenly causes the machine here and there to function differently than usual.'

"Kuyper does not want to put limits to the action of God, but he wants much more to recognize and to respect the activity of God to the fullest extent. His protest is lodged against every supposition 'as if nature is something which exists and runs and acts by itself, and as if God from outside, now and then, intervenes in the course of things.' In 'nature' there would then be an order factually independent of God, which would experience a breakthrough in the miracle through divine intervention. 'The error of supranaturalism is conquered only when every idea of such an independent and permanent existence of nature is eradicated root and branch; and when one grasps fully that both nature and all her forces and everyone of her laws, are nothing in themselves, but that they are what they are from moment to moment through the command that issues from the mouth of God.'

"Kuyper refuses thus definitely to see the miracle placed against the background of a mechanistic-monistically comprehended "nature," the abstraction of the rationalistic natural science that wanted to dominate the entire cosmos. *This* concept of "nature" in its irreligious character he has fathomed and rejected. Supranaturalism is renounced by him not from *naturalistic* motives, but this renunciation intends to proclaim the *divine transcendental* "supra" over all of reality. That is why he raises objection against the "incidental" intervention of God in the course of things, 'because nothing runs through a power outside of God' and 'the miracle thus may never be proposed as a disturbance or intervention. It is nothing else than that God at a certain moment wishes a certain thing differently, differently than it has been willed by Him thus far.' Berkouwer continues after some other quotations: "And in order, above all not to isolate the miracle, Kuyper arrives at the sharply delineated words when he calls the miracle: 'exactly the same as an ordinary act of nature; because it means both that a command went forth from the mouth of God and that *his*

servants, the elements and forces of nature, accomplished it thus.'
Kuyper distinguished sharply between the miraculous acts of God
and the wiles of the magician 'who displays now this and then that
in order to show his dexterity.' Not the caprice but the *will* of
God is the background of the miracle, which is not an incidental
intervention in a bound nature, but another — uncommon — method
of God's rule over all things. Summarizing, we can say that
Kuyper's opposition against supranaturalism arises from the *religious* protest against a kind of nature that is *independent* of God,
who then in the miracle gives the *break-through.*"[38]

From this part of Berkouwer's reproduction of Kuyper's views
it appears evident that the latter rejected supranaturalism radically.
He did this in regard to the problem of the miracle. It is entirely
in line to use the same reasoning, or to propose it as a possibility,
in connection with the problem of the origin of organisms. Often
the opinion is embraced that Kuyper in his treatise on Evolution
objected to this view. The well-known words with which he com-
menced, "Our nineteenth century dies away under the hypnosis of
the Evolution-dogma,"[39] has led astray many who have not studied
closely what follows in this discourse. The drift of Kuyper's
treatise is again a decided rejection of evolutionism as a materialistic doctrine of autonomous nature. It is "a newly thought-out
system, a newly coined doctrine, a newly formed dogma, a newly
arisen faith, which, comprising and dominating all our life, takes
its stand directly opposite the Christian faith and can erect its
temple only upon the ruins of our Christian Confession of Faith.
No sympathy with nor appreciation of all the beauty and wealth
that the studies it stimulated threw into our lap, for that reason,
may cause us even for moment to have peace with that system
as system. That system remains evil, even though also here from
evil in many respects good may result. And, therefore, against
that system of a cosmos built mechanically, without purpose, we
should register our opposition in every area."[40]

Thus Kuyper turns vehemently against "the system," but not in

---

[38] G. C. Berkouwer, *op. cit.*, 1950, pp. 238-239.
[39] A. Kuyper, *Evolutie*, Rectorale Oratie, Vrije Universiteit, 1899, p. 7.
[40] *Op. cit.*, p. 50.

the least does he consider the acceptance of the evolutionary phenomenon fundamentally unacceptable for the Christian faith.

An extensive quotation will show this plainly, clearly and indisputably: "An entirely different problem is that so often discussed in England whether religion permits, as such, the spontaneous evolvement of the species in the organic world from one single primary cell. That question, of course, without reservation, must be answered in the affirmative. We should not impose our style upon the Chief Architect of the universe. Provided he remains, not in appearance, but in essence, the Architect, he is also in the choice of his style of architecture the Omnipotent. If it thus had pleased the Lord not to create the species as such, but to have one species arise from the other, by designing the preceding species in such a way that it could produce the next higher, the creation would have been just as wonderful. But this never would have been the evolution of Darwinism because the predetermined plan [*Zweck*] would not then have been excluded, but would have been all-predominating, and not the world had then built itself up mechanically, but God by means of elements which He himself prepared for that purpose. The contrast shows itself most clearly from an illustration selected by Haeckel. In order to remove the objection that is inherent in the mechanical explanation of a complex organism, he asks whether a Zulu Negro, who at Lorenzo Marquez sees an English armored battleship enter, would not certainly view this colossus as an organic monster, while *we*, of course, know very well that it has been riveted together mechanically. Everyone naturally agrees with this. But Haeckel overlooked the fact that in the shipyard the steel plates did not *place themselves* in the proper position, but that they have been *put together* by a skillful architect according to a previously prepared plan. And that same difference would differentiate such a divine evolutionistic creation from the system of the Darwinists. Evolutionistic creation presupposes a God who has first made the plan and then executes it omnipotently. Darwinism teaches the mechanical origin of things that excludes all plan or purpose or draft."[41]

---

[41] *Op. cit.*, pp. 46-48.

Here we see plainly that Kuyper left open the possibility of a genetic relation between the organisms and that "without reservation" he designated this possibility as not in conflict with the Christian faith.

It is this profound insight into the situation of the real problems which has been lost sight of, regrettably, by many followers of Kuyper.

Many will in the very first place point out that Kuyper, it is true, left open this possibility, but did not himself propose this *positively* as possible; further, also, that he limited this eventual possibility of evolution to the evolvement of plants and animals, but that he certainly would not have applied this, for example, to the origin of life or of man.

As far as the first is concerned, that is a question of the quantity of the arguments. We should think of the fact that in Kuyper's day determination of the age of the earth by means of radioactive methods had not yet been developed, that the insight into the chemical structure of the organisms was yet extremely limited, that as yet only a few fossil hominid forms were known, that no one knew anything about prehistoric cultures, etc. The first argument, therefore, is not of principle value.

The second is more important. To this we can answer that Kuyper in connection with the passage cited above, "But this never would have been the evolution of Darwinism because the predetermined plan [*Zweck*] would not then have been excluded, but would have been all-predominating, and not the world had then built itself up mechanically, but God, by means of elements which He himself prepared for that purpose," placed the following footnote: "Du Bois-Reymond in his last address, *Neovitalismus*, 1894, actually accepts this. He proposes that God, 'unimaginably long ago, through *one* act of creation, created the totality of matter in such a way that according to the laws that were given with matter simple living beings originated from which, there came without any further aid, nature of today, from a primitive micrococcus to the charming features of Suleima and to Newton's brain.' This, however, is entirely in conflict with the doctrine of evolution and Haeckel, therefore, hastens to condemn this in his latest work, *Die Welträthsel*, Bonn, 1899, p. 274."

From this it is clear that Kuyper viewed as compatible with the Christian confession a general evolution from lifeless matter to man which was guided by God and began with *one* creation at the beginning. In our book this idea is stated more positively as a possibility, since none of the former classic views in Christian circles today can stand the test of criticism. Fundamentalism as well as supranaturalism appear to have originated from a partly philosophical accommodation to untenable speculative scientific hypotheses and pseudo-certainties.

Only when we learn to accept all occurrences as "miraculous" and *only* believe in the realities that have been revealed to us, can we see the problems in their proper proportions.

Our final conclusion concerning the problem of creation and evolution then can be none other than that not a single miracle can be demonstrated with any apparatus or can be made probable with any calculating machine or can be comprehended by the keenest intellect; whether that miracle be that of the creation of the entities of this total reality, which are essentially differentiated from one another, or that of the divine guidance by the evolving unfolding of the flora and fauna, of human life and culture, or of the re-creation in Jesus Christ. They are not amenable to sense-perception and they cannot be the object of experimentation. Thus they cannot be discovered by science, although all things and occurrences in this reality owe their origin, their existence and their direction to them. They are what Diemer calls "the incomprehensible deeds and the unsearchable ways of God." Man who is contained within this same reality can only "see" them via the function of faith through divine revelation. He does not have on that account more *data* than the non-believer, but he does see the data in another light. He himself together with all investigators has to collect the data of this reality in his scientific work. He must accept *all* data, before whatever problems they may place him, but he may not enlarge or diminish their significance through positive or negative speculations. He may arrange working hypotheses which are necessary for further investigation, provided he continues to view these hypotheses only as *possibilities*.

At the end of this writing the hope is expressed that, first of all, it has become evident that we as Christians must be in earnest about the problems before which natural science places man today, but further, that our faith does not hamper our science and even less that our faith has to be engaged in an irreconcilable conflict with the data we have at our disposal. It is much more true that the Christian has to gather and to study the data with an open and free interest.

Involuntarily our thoughts are directed to the beautiful Article II of the Belgic Confession of Faith: "We know him (God) by two means: First by the creation, preservation and government of the universe; which is before our eyes as a most elegant book, wherein all creatures, great and small, are as so many characters leading us to see clearly the invisible things of God, even his everlasting power and divinity." Remarkable: "eyes" that view "invisible things"! That means that every human being who directs his faith upon the only Savior of this reality, Jesus Christ, is going to see this creation again in a new light. "All creatures, great and small"; no datum may thus be disavowed and, freely and freed, we may try to wrest from the creation its secrets!

We can only do this to the honor of God by viewing them in the light of His revelation in Scripture. This is expressed in the conclusion of this Article II: "Secondly He makes Himself more clearly and fully known to us by His holy and divine Word, that is to say, as far as is necessary for us to know in this life, to His glory, and our salvation."

That is the important issue of Scripture. The Bible is thus no human-like technical scientific treatise about God's acts, but it reveals to us precisely so much of God and of His actions not discoverable by science as man, the crown of creation, needs in order that he can live again to God's honor. Thus he may experience, in reverent communion with God and his neighbor, that this apparently senseless, purposeless and accidental reality is indeed meaningful, planned and directed.

CHAPTER SEVEN
LITERATURE AND BIBLIOGRAPHY

G. C. Aalders, De Goddelijke openbaring in de eerste drie hoofdstukken van Genesis, Kampen, 1932.

L. Agassiz, De l'espèce et de la classification en zoologie, Paris, 1869.

L. Agassiz, Der Schöpfungsplan, 1875.

J. Alexander, Life. Its nature and origin, New York, 1948.

R. C. Andrews, Meet your ancestors, London, 1944; Ned. vert.: Apen, schedels en mensen, Rotterdam, 1952.

H. Bächler, Die ersten Bewohner der Schweiz, Bern, 1947.

G. Ballintijn, Rumphius, Utrecht, 1944.

F. C. Bawden, Plantviruses and virus diseases, Waltham, 1950.

G. R. de Beer, The evolution of Metazoa, in J. Huxley c.s., Evolution as a process, London, 1954.

P. G. Berkhout, Revelation and evolution. Geloof en Wetenschap, 55, pp. 166-176, 1957.

G. C. Berkouwer, De voorzienigheid Gods, Kampen, 1950.

J. Bernal, The physical basis of life, London, 1952.

J. Bernal, The origin of life, New Biology, 16, 28—40, 1954.

N. J. Berrill, The origin of vertebrates, Oxford, 1955.

L. von Bertalanffy, Theoretische Biologie I, Berlin, 1932.

J. A. Bierens de Haan, Die tierischen Instinkte und ihre Umbau durch Erfahrung, Leiden, 1940.

H. Böker, Einführung in die Vergleichende Biologische Anatomie der Wirbeltiere I en II, Jena, 1935—'37.

H. Böker, Artumwandlung durch Umkonstruktion, Umkonstruktion durch aktives Reagieren der Organismen, Acta Biotheoretica, 1, 17—34, 1935.

H. L. Booy, Aan de grens van het leven, Leiden, 1947.

L. A. Borradaile c.s., The Invertebrata, 2nd ed., Cambridge, 1948.
H. Boschma, Het soortbegrip, Inaug. Oratie, Leiden, 1931.
M. Boule et H.V. Vallois, Les hommes fossiles, 4e ed., Paris, 1952.
H. Breuil, Die ältere und mittlere Altsteinzeit Alt- und Mittelpaläolithikum, Historia N
    Bern, 259—288, 1952.
H. J. T. Bijlmer, De evolutie van de mens, 's-Gravenhage, 1946.
G. S. Carter, A general zoology of the invertebrates, London, 1948.
R. E. D. Clark, Darwin: before and after, London, 1948. Grand Rapids, 1958.
P. E. Cloud Jr, Some problems and patterns of evolution exemplified by fossil invertebrates
    Evolution, 2, 322—350, 1948.
S. Cole, The prehistory of East Africa, London, 1954.
W. A. Collier, Hypothesen over de oorsprong van virus en virus-soorten, Chronica Naturae
    no. 105, p. 11, 1949.
H. Conrad-Martius, Abstammungslehre, München, 1949.
L. Cuénot, l'Espèce, Paris, 1936.
G. Cuvier, Le règne animal; Les mammifères, Paris, 1828.
B. H. Danser, Over het soortbegrip in de Plant- en Dierkunde, Hand. v. h. 4e Ned. Ind. Natuur
    wetenschappelijk Congres, 1926, p. 347.
R. Dart, The osteodontokeratic culture of Australopithecus Prometheus, Pretoria, 1957.
Ch. Darwin, Variation of animals and plants under domestication, London, 1868.
Ch. Darwin, Autobiography, The Thinkers Library no. 7, 6e ed., London, 1949.
F. Darwin, Life and Letters of Charles Darwin, I, II, III, London, 1887.
D. D. Davis, Comparative anatomy and the evolution of vertebrates, in „Genetics, paleontology,
    and evolution", Princeton, 1949.
J. H. Diemer, Over biotypen van *Annopheles maculipennis* Meigen, in het bijzonder in Westelijk
    Nederland, Dissertatie Leiden, 1935
J. H. Diemer, Ingezonden stuk, De Standaard, 20 Febr. 1939.
J. H. Diemer, De totaliteit van het leven, Calvinistisch Weekblad, 6, 78, 86, 1940.
J. H. Diemer, De „dagen" in het scheppingsverhaal, Calvinistisch Studentenblad, 6 (3), 1—6,
    1942.   Appears also in Sola Fide, 7 (1), 7—12, 1953.
J. H. Diemer, Natuur en Wonder, Philosophia Reformata, 8, 100—128, 1943; 9, 42—61, 1944.
J. H. Diemer, Natuur en Wonder, Org. v. d. Chr. Ver. v. Nat.- en Geneesk. i. Nederland,
    53—92, 1944.
H. Dooyeweerd, De Wijsbegeerte der Wetsidee I, II, III, Amsterdam, 1935—'36.
H. Dooyeweerd, De leer van den mensch in de Wijsbegeerte der Wetsidee, Correspondentie-
    bladen van de Vereniging voor Calvinistische Wijsbegeerte, 7 (5), 133—143, 1942.
H. Dooyeweerd, Het substantiebegrip in de moderne natuurphilosophie en de theorie van het
    enkaptisch structuurgeheel, Philosophie Reformata, 15, 66—139, 1950.
H. Dooyeweerd, A new critique of theoretical thought, 3 vols., Philadelphia, 1953, 1955, 1957.
H. Dooyeweerd, Transcendental problems of philosophic thought, Grand Rapids, 1948.
H. Driesch, Philosophie des Organischen, 2 dln., Leipzig, 1909.
E. Dubois, *Pithecanthropus erectus*, eine menschenaehnliche Uebergangsform aus Java, Batavia,
    1894.
J. J. Duyvené de Wit, Gezichtspunten voor een integratieve biologische wetenschapsbeschou-
    wing, Inaug. oratie Vrije Universiteit, 1950.
F. Falkenburger, Kritische Bemerkungen zur Entwicklung des Sapienstypus, Actes du IVe Con-
    grès International des Sciences Anthropol. et Ethnol., I, 105—106, 1954.
R. H. Flower, Saltations in Nautiloid coiling, Evolution, 9, 245—260, 1955.
H. Frieling, Was ist der Mensch? Bamberg, 1948.

R. Goldschmidt, The material basis of evolution, New Haven, 1940.

W. K. Gregory, Evolution emerging, I en II, New York, 1951.

P. Groen, Over de grenzen der voorspelbaarheid in de natuur, Inaug. Oratie Vrije Universiteit, 1952.

E. Haeckel, Systematische Phylogenie I, II, III, Berlin, 1894—'95.

E. Haeckel, Natürliche Schöpfungsgeschichte, 12e ed., Berlin, 1920.

E. Haeckel, Das Weltbild von Darwin und Lamarck, Leipzig, 1909.

A. C. Hardy, On the origin of Metazoa, Q.J. M. S., 94, 441—443, 1953.

G. Heberer, Neue Ergebnisse der menschlichen Abstammungslehre, Göttingen, 1951.

V. Hepp, Calvinism and the philosophy of nature, Grand Rapids, 1930.

J. H. E. J. Hoogveld, Inleiding tot leven en leer van S. Thomas van Aquino, Nijmegen, 1939.

E. A. Hooton, Up from the ape, 4e ed., New York, 1946.

J. Huxley c.s., The new systematics, Oxford, 1940.

J. Huxley, Soviet genetics: the real issue I, II, Nature, 163, 935, 974, 1949.

J. Huxley, Soviet genetics and world science, London, 1949.

J. Huxley, A. C. Hardy and E. B. Ford, Evolution as a process, London, 1954.

L. Huxley, Thomas Henry Huxley, London, 1920.

C. L. Hubbs, Racial and individual variation in animals, especially fishes, Amer. Nat., 68, 115—128, 1934.

J. E. W. Ihle en H. F. Nierstrasz e.a., Leerboek der Bijzondere Dierkunde, Utrecht, 1928.

E. O. James, Prehistoric religion. London, 1957.

G. L. Jepsen, G. G. Simpson and E. Mayr, Genetics, Paleontology and Evolution, Princeton, 1949.

H. J. Jordan, De causale verklaring van het leven, Amsterdam, 1940.

J. Kälin, Zum Problem der menschlichen Stammesgeschichte, Experientia, 2, 272—287, 1946.

J. Kälin, Die ältesten Menschenreste und ihre stammesgeschichtliche Deutung, Historia Mundi I, Bern, 33—98, 1952.

O. Kleinschmidt, Die Formenkreislehre und das Weltwerden des Lebens, 1926.

J. P. Kleiweg de Zwaan, De oudste mensheid in Europa en Indonesië, 's-Gravenhage, 1955.

A. Knopf, Time in earth history, in: G. L. Jepsen, G. G. Simpson and E. Mayr, Genetics, paleontology, and evolution, Princeton, p. 1—19, 1949.

G. H. R. von Koenigswald, The discovery of early man in Java and Southern China, Studies in Physical Anthropology, 1, 83—98, 1949.

G. H. R. von Koenigswald, *Giganthopithecus blacki* von Koenigswald, a giant fossil Hominoid from the Pleistocene of Southern China, Anthr. Papers Amer. Mus. Nat. Hist., 43, 295—325, 1952.

G. H. R. von Koenigswald, Die Phylogenie des Menschen, Die Naturwissenschaften, 40, 128—137, 1953.

G. H. R. von Koenigswald, The Australopithecinae and *Pithecanthropus* I, II, III, Proceedings Kon. Ned. Akad. v. Wetensch. Series B, 56, 403—413, 427—438, 1953; 57, 85—91, 1954.

G. H. R. von Koenigswald, *Pithecanthropus, Meganthropus*, and the Australopithecinae, Nature, 173, 795, 1954.

W. Koppers, Der Urmensch und sein Weltbild, Wien, 1949.

. Kramp, Zur Abstammung des Menschen, in: Schöpfungsglaube und Evolutionstheorie, Stuttgart, 1955.

O. Kuhn, Typologische Betrachtungsweise und Paläontologie, Acta Biotheoretica, 6, 55—96, 1942.

O. Kuhn, Lehrbuch der Paläozoologie, Stuttgart, 1949.

O. Kuhn, Die Deszendenztheorie, München, 1951.

H. Kühn, Das Erwachen der Menschheit, Frankfurt, 1954.
H. Kühn, Die Kunst Alteuropas, Stuttgart, 1954.
H. Kühn, Der Aufstieg der Menschheit, Frankfurt, 1955.
H. Kühn, Eiszeitmalerei, München, 1956.
A. Kuyper, Evolutie, Rectorale Oratie Vrije Universiteit, Amsterdam, 1899.
H. J. Lam, Evolutie, Leiden, 1946.
J. B. de Lamarck, Philosophie Zoologique, Paris, Ed. 1907.
E. Lankester, Memorials of John Ray, London, 1844.
L. S. B. Leakey, Adam's ancestors, London, 4e ed., 1953.
P. Lecomte du Noüy, Human destiny. Ned. Vert.: Wij en onze bestemming, Amsterdam, 1948.
W. E. Le Gros Clark, History of the primates, 3e ed., London, 1953.
G. W. Leibniz, Hauptschriften zur Grundlegung der Philosophie, Philosophische Bibliothek, Bd. 108, Leipzig, 1906.
J. Lever en H. Dooyeweerd, Rondom het biologisch soortbegrip, Philosophia Reformata, 13, 119—138, 1948; 14, 6—32, 1949; 15, 1—23, 1950.
J. Lever, Onderzoekingen betreffende de schildklierstructuur, Diss. Utrecht, 1950.
J. Lever, Het soortbegrip en de levende structuren, Openbare Les Vrije Universiteit, 1950.
J. Lever, Het vraagstuk der typenafleidbaarheid tegen de achtergrond van de geschiedenis van de evolutietheorie, Geloof en Wetenschap, 50, 13—27, 1952.
J. Lever, Het creationisme, Inaug. oratie Vrije Universiteit, 1952.
J. Lever, Charles Robert Darwin, Geloof en Wetenschap, 51, 67—91, 1953.
J. Lever, De biosynthese van het schildklierhormoon, Vakblad voor Biologen, 34, 24—31, 1954
J. Lever, Ewolusionisme en Kreasionisme in die biologie, Tydskrif vir Wetenskap en Kuns, 13 211—270, 1953; 14, 63—96, 1954.
J. Lever. De mens in de biologie, Geloof en Wetenschap, 52, 77—100, 1954.
J. Lever, De oorsprong van de mens, Geloof en Wetenschap, 53, 133—161, 1955.
I. Lichtig, Entstehung des Lebens durch stetige Schöpfung, Amsterdam, 1938.
K. Lorenz, Ueber den Begriff der Instinkthandlung, Folia Biotheoretica, 2, 17—50, 1937.
J. P. Lotsy, Evolution im Lichte der Bastardierung betrachtet, 's-Gravenhage, 1926.
J. P. Lotsy. Evolution considered in the light of hybridization. Christchurch, New Zealand Printed for Canterbury College by Andrews, Baty & Co., Ltd., 1925.
W. Lubosch, Geschichte der vergleichenden Anatomie, in Bolk c.s. Handbuch der vergleichenden Anatomie der Wirbeltiere I, Berlin, 1931.
J. Maringer and H. G. Bandi, Art in the ice-age, Basel, 1953.
E. Mayr, Systematics and the origin of species, New York, 1942.
E. Mayr, The bearing of the New Systematics on genetical problems; the nature of species Advances in Genetics, 2, 205—237, 1948.
A. Meyer-Abich, Logik der Morphologie, Berlin, 1926.
A. Meyer-Abich, Ideen und Ideale der biologischen Erkenntnis, Leipzig, 1934.
A. Meyer-Abich, Krisenepochen und Wendepunkte des biologischen Denkens, Jena, 1935.
A. Meyer-Abich, Hauptgedanken des Holismus, Acta Biotheoretica, 5, 85—116, 1939.
A. Meyer-Abich, Beiträge zur Theorie der Evolution der Organismen. I. Das typologisch Grundgesetz und seine Folgerungen für Phylogenie und Entwicklungsphysiologie, Act Biotheoretica, 7, 1—80, 1943.
A. Meyer-Abich, Naturphilosophie auf neuen Wegen, Stuttgart, 1948.
S. L. Miller, A production of aminoacids under possible primitive earth conditions, Science 117, 528—529, 1953.
K. Möbius, Die Bildung, Geltung und Bezeichnung der Artbegriffe und ihr Verhältnis zu Abstammungslehre, Jena, 1886.

W. A. Mohler, Zur Stratigraphie der säugetierführenden Schichten von Java, Experientia, **2**, 287—292, 1946.

E. Y. Monsma, If not evolution, what then? Grand Rapids, 1954.

H. J. Muller, Life, Science, **121**, 1—9, 1955.

H. Munro Fox, Chemical taxonomy, Nature, **157**, 511, 1946.

A. Naef, Die individuelle Entwicklung organischer Formen als Urkunde ihrer Stammesgeschichte, Jena, 1917.

A. Naef, Idealistische Morphologie und Genetik, Jena, 1919.

L. M. van Nieuwenhoven S. J., Biologie, Roermond, 1954.

N. Heribert-Nilsson, Der Entwicklungsgedanke und die moderne Biologie (Bios Bd. 13), Leipzig, 1938.

K. P. Oakley, Man the tool-maker, 2e ed., London, 1952.

G. J. van Oordt, Ueber einen biologischen Unterschied zwischen Fluss- und Küstenseeschwalbe (*Sterna hirundo* und *Sterna paradisea*), Beitr. z. Fortpflanzungsbiologie der Vögel, **10**, p. 5, 1934

A. I. Oparin, The origin of Life, New York, 1938.

A. I. Oparin, Das Problem der Entstehung des Lebens im Lichte der modernen Naturwissenschaft, Sowjetwissenschaft (Naturw. Abt.), **7**, 299—309, 1954.

G. Penso, Cycle of phage development within the bacterial cell, Protoplasma, **45**, 251—263, 1955.

N. W. Pirie, On making and recognizing life, New Biology, **16**, 41—53, 1954.

L. Plate, Utramontane Weltanschauung und moderne Lebenskunde, Orthodoxie und Monismus, Jena, 1907.

A. Portmann, Vom Ursprung des Menschen, Basel, 1944.

A. Portman, Von der Idee des Humanen in der gegenwärtigen Biologie, St. Gallen, 1951.

A. Portmann, Biologische Fragmente zu einer Lehre vom Menschen, Basel, 1951.

J. W. S. Pringle, The evolution of living matter, New Biology, **16**, 54—67, 1954.

E. Radl, Geschichte der biologischen Theorien in der Neuzeit I, Leipzig, 1913.

B. Ramm, The christian view of Science and Scripture, Michigan, 1955.

B. Rensch, Neuere Probleme der Abstammungslehre, Stuttgart, 1947.

N. H. Ridderbos, Beschouwingen over Genesis 1, Assen, 1954.   Free University Quarterly, 4, 221-235, 1957.

J. T. Robinson, Prehominid dentition and hominid evolution, Evolution, **8**, 324—334, 1954.

A. S. Romer, Man and the Vertebrates, 7e ed., Chicago, 1948.

A. S. Romer, Vertebrate Paleontology, 4e ed., Chicago, 1950.

A. Rust, Die jüngere Altsteinzeit Jungpaläolithikum, Historia Mundi I, Bern, 289—317, 1952.

M. G. Rutten, Actualisme en evolutie. Inaug. Oratie, Utrecht, 1951.

F. Sassen, Geschiedenis der patristische en middeleeuwse wijsbegeerte, 1942.

O. Schindewolf, Beobachtungen und Gedanken zur Deszendenzlehre, Acta Biotheoretica, **3**, 195—212, 1937.

O. Schindewolf, Grundfragen der Paläontologie, Stuttgart, 1950.

O. Schindewolf, Der Zeitfaktor in Geologie und Paläontologie, Stuttgart, 1950.

P. W. Schmidt, Die Urkulturen: Ältere Jagd- und Sammelstufe, Historia Mundi I, Bern, 375—501, 1952.

I. Schmutzer, Prof. Ernst Haeckel, Leiden, 1907.

O. Schoetensack, Der Unterkiefer des *Homo heidelbergensis*, Leipzig, 1908.

A. H. Schultz, Origin of the human stock. The specializations of man and his place among the Catarrhine Primates, Cold Spring Harbor Symposia on Quantitative Biology, **15**, 37—53, 1950.

G. G. Simpson, Tempo and mode in evolution, New York, 1947.

G. G. Simpson, The meaning of evolution, 4e ed., New Haven, 1950.

G. J. Sizoo, De herziening van het physische causaliteitsbeginsel. Rectorale Oratie Vrije Universiteit, 1952.

G. J. Sizoo e.a., De ouderdom der aarde, 4e ed., Kampen, 1955.

W. A. Smalley and M. Fetzer, A christian view of anthropology, in: Modern Science and Christian faith, Wheaton, 98—195, 1950.

M. C. Smit, Het Goddelijk geheim in de geschiedenis. Inaug. Oratie Vrije Universiteit, 1955.

P. W. Stoner, Science speaks, Wheaton, 1952.

J. Theunisz, Carolus Clusius, Amsterdam, 1939.

T. H. Thung, Grondbeginselen der Plantenvirologie, Wageningen, 1949.

N. Tinbergen, An objectivistic study of the innate behaviour of animals, Bibliotheca Biotheoretica, **1**, 39—98, 1942.

W. Troll, Das Virusproblem in ontologischer Sicht, Wiesbaden, 1951.

E. Uhlmann, Entwicklungsgedanke und Artbegriff, Jena, 1923.

J. Valckenier Suringar, De geschiedenis der verwantschapsidee in het plantenrijk, Mededelingen v. d. Landbouwhogeschool te Wageningen, **36**, (1) 3—62 en (2) 3—53, 1932.

L. Verduin, Toward a theistic creationism, Geloof en Wetenschap, 54, 183-198, 1956. Also Grand Rapids, 1957.

K. H. Voous, Het soortbegrip in de zoögeographie, Biol. Jaarb. „Dodonaea", **16**, 157—167, 1949.

K. H. Voous, Het soortbegrip in de zoögeographie, Hand v. h. 31e Ned. Nat.- en Geneesk. Congres, p. 115—116, 1949.

K. H. Voous, Zoögeographie en evolutie, Vakblad v. Biologen, **30**, 155—164, 1950.

H. de Vries, Intracellulare Pangenesis, 1889, in Opera e periodicis collata V, Utrecht, 1920.

H. de Vries, Experimentele evolutie, Amsterdam, z.j.

J. de Vries, Beyond the atom, Grand Rapids, 1948.

G. Wald, The origin of life, Scientific American, **191**, 45—53, 1954.

E. Wasmann, Die moderne Biologie und die Entwicklungstheorie, Freiburg, 1904.

F. Weidenreich, The human brain in the light of its phylogenetic development, The Scientific Monthly, **67**, 103—109, 1948.

F. Weidenreich, Apes, giants, and man, 4e ed,. Chicago, 1948.

F. Weidenreich, Interpretations of the fossil material, Studies in Physical Anthropol., **1**, 149—157, 1919.

H. Weinert, Entstehung der Menschenrassen, Stuttgart, 1941.

H. Weinert, Ursprung der Menschheit, Stuttgart, 1944.

H. Weinert, Der geistige Aufstieg der Menschheit, 2e ed., Stuttgart, 1951.

H. Weinert, Stammesentwicklung der Menschheit, Braunschweig, 1951.

A. Weismann, Die Continuität des Keimplasmas, Jena, 1892.

M. Westenhöfer, Die Grundlagen meiner Theorie vom Eigenweg des Menschen, Heidelberg, 1948.

M. J. D. White, Animal cytology and evolution, 1945.

A. Wigand, Der Darwinismus und die Naturforschung Newtons und Cuviers I, II, III, Braunschweig, 1874-1877.

H. R. Woltjer, The age of the earth, Free Univ. Quart., **3**, 188—204, 1955.

F. E. Zeuner, Dating the past, 3e ed., London, 1952.

W. Zimmermann, Evolution, Freiburg/München, 1953.

INDEX

Aalders, G. C., 17, 18, 19

Agassiz, Louis, his opposition to evolution, 74; pupil of Cuvier, 74; 84

Albertus Magnus, peculiar views on transformation of organisms, 60-61; 110; universalia, 104; Ray compared to him, 107

Aldrovandi, 105

Anaxagoras, 28, 29, 34, 43

Andrews, R. C., 163

Aquinas, Thomas, and Aristotle, 103; and realism, 104; universalia, 104; Ray compared to him, 107; views on the miracle, 210

Aristotle, on origin of life, 28-29; on genus and species, 102; on realism, 103; 105

Augustine, St., on spontaneous generation, 30-31; 64; on creation and providence, 209; on the miracle, 209

Australopithecinae, 154, 155, 159, 182; relation to man, 194-195

Berkhout, P. G., in footnote, 226

Berkouwer, G. C., on A. Kuyper, 226-228

Bertalanffy, L. von, 52

Böker, H., on problem of sudden appearance of types, 85; "transformation of species through reconstruction," 87-89

Bonnet, devotee of Leibniz, 69-70

Borradaille, L. A., on Haeckelian reasoning about origin of molluscs, 73

Boschma, on definition of species, 124

Boutroux, Emile, influence on A. Meyer, 130

Brain, large brain no sign of intelligence, 158; of geniuses, 159

Brunfels, the "Father of Botany," 105

Buchner, on miracle, 212

Buffon, 34

Bijlmer, H. J. T., 182, 183

Caesalpinus, built his Aristotelian system upon really vital functions, 105; sought for natural system, 105

Carter, G. S., on absence of links, 78

Clark, R. E. D., idea of fixity of species not attributable to Christianity, 110

Cloud, P. E., Jr. on fossil algae, 77

Clusius, his basis of division of plants, 105

Conrad-Martius, Hedwig, 206

Constancy of species, idea in Middle Ages, 60; peculiar views against it by Christians, 61; Cuvier, 64-65; John

Ray, 107; Linnaeus, 108, 111; and Christianity, 110; Hugo De Vries, 118; no constancy, 122; 137

Creationism, definition, 26; vs. evolution, 56-57; description, 58, 76; vs. fortuity, 96; evolution subservient to, 98; were phyla created?, 98-99; John Ray's view, 107; Linnaeus, 205

Cuénot, 111; on chromosomes, 121

Culture, cultural objects the only guides for spiritual life, 154

Cuvier, George, 64; his four types, 65; his general plan, 67; theory of catastrophes, 69; Agassiz his pupil, 74; Nilsson's comment on, 82; Lyell vs. Cuvier, 86; right if phyla arose independently, 99

Danser, B. H., syngameon, 124; 126

Darwin, Charles, 12-13; 16; 20; on spontaneous generation, 38; on morphology, 41; opposed by Agassiz, 74; favors Lyell, 86; pangenesis, 115, 116, 117, 138, 204

Davis, D. D., sudden appearance of types, 85

DeVries, Hugo, on species, 111, 112, 116; mutation theory, 118, 122

De Vries, John, in footnote, 19

Diemer, J. H., on nominalism, 103; on Ray, 106, 122; on mechanism, vitalism and holism, 129; follower of Dooyeweerd, 134; on miracle, 209-221

Dioscorides, his flora, 105

Dooyeweerd, H., philosophy of the cosmonomic idea, 129, 130; applied to endocrine functions, 131-134; only the heart supra-temporal, 192; on individuality structures, 193-194

Driesch, H., 122; neo-vitalism, 128, 129

Dubois, E., 143, 144, 145, 146, 180, 190

Earth, meaning of, 17; cold origin, 51

Evolution, lex continui became its law, 70; classic evolutionism, 74; opposed by Agassiz, 74; by Wigand, 75; origin of molluscs, 78; of vertebrates, 79; of Metazoa from Metaphyta, 80; importance of paleontology, 80; classic evolutionism, 81; ev. of fish, 83; Kuhn vs. classic ev., 83; problem of sudden appearance of types, 85; neo-evolutionism, 86-91; ev. of classes, 94; Christians may believe that mammals evolved from reptiles and amphibians, 97; Lamarck's views, 111-115; brought out man's difference from the animals, 192; his views based on faith, 203 ff.

241

INDEX

Locke, John, nominalism, 104; on John Ray, 106
Lorenz, K., and *Columbidae*, 134-135
Lotsy, J. P., on Alexis Jordan, 120-121, 124
Lubosch, W,, on unity of plan of Geoffry St. Hilaire, 66; typologist, 122
Lyell, Charles, his uniformitarianism basis for classic evolutionism, 86; rejected, 86, 92, 147

Myer, E., on sudden appearance of types, 85; on species, 124
Mechanism, 14, 36, 43, 127; description of, 128; Diemer's view on, 129, 137
Meganthropus africanus, 152, 195
Meganthropus paleojavanicus, 152, 153
Mendel, G., 117
Meyer-Abich, Adolph, on theory that life always existed, 44; neo-evolutionism always to search for new possibilities of descent, 87; holobiosis, 91, 110; typology, 123; on systematics, 125, 127; holist, 129-130
Miller, S. L., on origin of life, 46
Miracle, Diemer's view, 209 ff.; St. Augustine, 210; Aquinas, 210; Reformation, 211; Spinoza, 211; Leibniz, 211-212; Kant, 212; Buchner, 212; Haeckel, 212; and supernaturalism and rationalism, 213; definition by Diemer, 214; Diemer's threefold view, 214-218; Sizoo, 225; in Egypt, etc., 225-226; A. Kuyper, 226-228; not explainable, 231
Möbius, K., 116
Monsma, E. Y., in footnote, 17

Naef, A., typology, 122, 125
Naegeli, C., 52
Needham, 34
Nidicolous and nidifugous animals, 184-188
Nillsson, Heribert, origin of plants, 81-82; vs. creation, 126
Nominalism, 102; definition, 103; Locke, 104; John Ray, 106; new nominalism, 119-120; critical nominalism, 123; of Leibniz, 211

Oakley, K. P., 162
Oparin, A. I., 47, 48
Origin of life, 42; from meteorites, 45; no new life originates on earth, 202; view of Hedwig Conrad-Martius, 206 ff., may have come from lifeless, 219; A. Kuyper's view, 288

Origin of man, 180 ff.; difference between man and anthropoids, 189 ff.; phylogenetic relation to anthropoids, 194; from the earth, 196; from an animal?, 197, 202; St. Augustine's view, 209; man may have genetic relation to animal, 221; A. Kuyper's view, 230

Paleontology, its importance compared with comparative anatomy and embryology, 73; importance according to Schindewolf, 80; origin of subgroups of vertebrates, 82-83; Kuhn on paucity of record, 83
Paracelsus, on spontaneous generation, 31-32
Pasteur, L., 35
Pithecanthropus erectus, 144, 145, 146, 149, 151, 153, 157, 159, 161, 190, 195, 199
Pithecanthropus robustus, 146, 149, 153
Plato, 64; on constancy of species, 110
Porphyrius, 102; on genus and species, 103
Portmann, 11, 27, 183, 190; on difference between man and recent anthropoids, 194, 202, 204
Pre-Adamites, 172
Precipitation blood-tests, 181
Preyer, life originated from the living, 43
"Primitialopfer," 168, 176, 1778
Proconsul, 157

Radl, E., on Albertus Magnus, 60-61; on Porphyrius, 103; on typology, 122
Ramm, B., in footnote, 18, 26; believes in fiat creation, 208
Ray, John, theologian and naturalist, 106; viewed by Diemer, 106; his form-principle and hybridization-principle, 107; constancy of species, 107; 123, 124, 125, 126, 135-136, 138
Realism, 102; ultra-realism, 103; moderate realism, 103; John Ray, 106; and pseudo-realism, 119-120; and typology 121; of Aquinas, 104
Redi, 33
Religion of pre-historic man, 163-170; pool of bones, 169-170
Remane, his definition of species, 124
Ridderbos, N. H., in footnote, 16
Rumphius, his principle of utility, 105
Rust, A., 169

Schindewolf, O., on importance of paleontology, 80; on sudden appearance of types, 85; thinks transitional forms